Diverse C Short Stories

Jean Moore and John Catron

Hodder & Stoughton

A MEMBER OF THE HODDER HEADLINE GROUP

Acknowledgements
The publishers would like to thank the following for their kind permission to
reproduce copyright material:

Copyright Text
p.9 *The Peacelike Mongoose* by James Thurber, from *Further Fables For Our Time* ©
1956 by James Thurber. Copyright renewed 1984 by Rosemary A. Thurber. Reprinted by
arrangement with Rosemary A. Thurber and The Barbara Hogenson Agency. All rights
reserved; p.15 *Frankie Mae* by Jean Wheeler Smith, from *Frankie Mae and Other Stories*
by Ann Mann and Hillary Rich; p.31 *Invisible Mass of the Back Row* by Claudette
Williams; p.45 *Deeper than Colour* by Ijeoma Inyama, published in *The Penguin Book of
New Black Writing in Britain* © Ijeoma Inyama; p.55 *Snowdrop* by Mei Chi Chan © Mei
Chi Chan; p.61 *On the Sidewalk Bleeding* by Evan Hunter. Reproduced with permission
of Curtis Brown Ltd, London on behalf of Hui Corporation © 1956, 1984 Evan Hunter;
p.71 *The Ones who Walk Away from Omelas* by Ursula Le Guin © 1973, 2001 by Ursula
Le Guin; first appeared in *New Dimensions 3*; from *The Winds Twelve Quarters*;
reprinted by permission of the author and the author's agents, the Virginia Kidd Agency,
Inc.; p.81 *Two Islands* by Ivan Gantschev. Die grüne & die graue Insel von Ivan
Gantschev © 1985, Michael Neugebauer Verlag, Velagsgruppe Nord-Süd Verlag AG,
Gossau Zürich/Schweiz; p.89 *The Assignment* by Saadat Hasan Manto from the collection
of *Stories From Asia*; p.97 *Free Dinners* by Farrukh Dhondy from *Come to Mecca*.
Reproduced with permission of David Higham Associates; p.113 *War of the Worlds* by
Ravinder Randhawa © Ravinder Randhawa; p.125 *Uproar* by Paul Wu, first published in
Dim Sum (British Chinese Short Stories) Crocus 1997 © Paul Wu; p.133 *About the
Wedding Feast* by Ama Ata Aidoo © Ama Ata Aidoo.

Illustrations
John Williams pp. 10, 12, 16, 18, 32, 34, 46, 48, 56, 58, 62, 64, 72, 74, 82, 84, 90, 92, 98,
114, 116, 126, 128, 134, 136.

Every effort has been made to trace copyright holders of material reproduced in this
book. Any rights not acknowledged will be acknowledged in subsequent printings if
notice is given to the publisher.

Orders: please contact Bookpoint Ltd, 130 Milton Park, Abingdon, Oxon OX14 4SB.
Telephone: (44) 01235 827720, Fax: (44) 01235 400454. Lines are open from 9.00am –
6.00pm, Monday to Saturday, with a 24 hour message answering service. Email address:
orders@bookpoint.co.uk

British Library Cataloguing in Publication Data
A catalogue record for this title is available from The British Library

ISBN 0 340 80296 0

First published   2001
Impression number 10 9 8 7 6 5 4 3 2 1
Year   2008 2007 2006 2005 2004 2003 2002 2001

Copyright © 2001 Jean Moore and John Catron

Cover photo from Holt Studios
Typeset by Fakenham Photosetting Limited, Fakenham, Norfolk
Printed in Great Britain for Hodder & Stoughton Educational, a division of Hodder
Headline Plc, 338 Euston Road, London NW1 3BH by The Bath Press, Bath.

CONTENTS

*Please note these stories contain strong language.

INTRODUCTION

The stories in this anthology were chosen from those that we knew worked well in the classroom, or that we recognised would do so. We also felt that each one provided a powerful and memorable way of examining culture in its widest sense, as well as creating opportunities for related literacy work, following the guidelines of the new Key Stage 3 framework.

It was also important that the stories should provide readers with insights into a variety of different characters, their voices and language, their homes, families and social groups, many of which will relate directly to the concerns and lives of the young people in schools today. There are many common themes: intolerance and prejudice, independence and isolation, courage and self confidence, all of which offer opportunities for Drama work, for writing and reading tasks and for varied speaking and listening activities. We hope that you will be as interested and inspired by these stories as we have been.

Using This Anthology

Each short story is preceded by a list of suggested outcomes, including those directly linked to word, sentence and text level work.

The links with the photocopiable pages in the related Teacher's Book are indicated by the symbol in the margin.

TB

The stimulus pages suggest areas for discussion or research before beginning the story. There are also snippets of information, tips on what to look for as you read, and questions to consider, all designed to enhance your reading of the story that follows.

THE WRITERS

James Thurber

James Thurber was born in Columbus, Ohio in 1894. He is famous as a humorist and artist, as well as a writer, and his work often contains sadness and resignation, as well as wry humour. His writing takes the form of stories, fables and essays; one of his most famous stories being *The Secret Life of Walter Mitty*. He was educated at Ohio State University, where he gained a degree in 1919, but his studies were affected by the fact that he was blind in one eye, the result of a childhood accident. He worked in Washington, Paris and New York, where he wrote articles for the *New Yorker* magazine for many years. He died in 1961.

Ijeoma Inyama

Ijeoma Injama was born on the 7th October, 1967, in London, UK. His previous published works are a short story, *Stephanie Brewster* published by Livewire in the collection *School Tales* in 1990, *Sistas on a Vibe*, a full length novel published in 1998, and the story included here, *Deeper than Colour*, originally published in 2000 in *The Penguin Book of New Black Writing in Britain*. He currently lives in Paris, and is writing his second novel.

Mei Chi Chan

Mei Chi Chan was born in Hong Kong in 1967. Her family moved to Nigeria for five years, before immigrating to Britain in 1974. They ran a restaurant, and then a takeaway in the Midlands. After receiving a first in Philosophy at the University of Lancaster, she worked as a creative writing liaison officer in Liverpool. She spent some time in Taiwan studying Tai Chi, and her interest in Buddhism led her to live for three years in monasteries in England and Thailand. She is now following a course in Buddhist-based psychotherapy, and runs Tai Chi classes in the south of England.

Evan Hunter (Ed McBain)

Evan Hunter (whose real name was Salvatore Lombino) was born in 1926 in New York. He has written under various names, the most famous of which is Ed McBain, and several of his books have been made into films. His novel *The Blackboard Jungle* was made into a film in 1955, and he also wrote the screenplay for Hitchcock's *The Birds*. He has written several novels on the theme of family tensions between generations, but is best known as a writer of crime fiction, under the name Ed McBain. Nearly all of these books are novels about police procedure set in the 87th precinct of a city very much like New York. He has also written children's stories, several powerful short stories and stage plays.

Ursula Le Guin

Ursula Le Guin was born in 1929. Her father was an anthropologist and her mother a writer of children's stories. The first story she sent to publishers was a science fiction story, written when she was only 11 years old! She studied Literature at Radcliffe, where she gained a degree, and then studied for her M.A. at Columbia University in Canada. She then went to study in France where she met the man who was to be her husband, Charles Le Guin. She writes science fiction and fantasy novels, short stories, children's stories, poetry and non-fiction, and several of her books have been used in British schools for many years. One critic said that some of her novels are 'philosophy disguised as science fiction'. She now lives in Portland, Oregon.

Ivan Gantschev

Ivan Gantschev was born in Tirnovo, Bulgaria. His father was a lawyer and his mother a teacher. The Second World War broke out while he was studying painting and graphic design at the Art Academy in Sofia, and his father encountered problems with the Bulgarian Fascists because he was a member of the Peasant's Party and later a Socialist. In 1944, Gantschev's father was deported and killed. In 1949 there were purges of colleges and universities, and Gantschev and seven of his fellow students were drafted into the Workers' Army for 18 months. Eventually, he was allowed to become a member of the artists' trade union and he subsequently worked as a graphic designer. In 1965 he was allowed to leave Bulgaria, and eventually got a job in West Germany. He has written and illustrated many books, and has been a German citizen since 1980.

Saadat Hasan Manto

Saadat Hasan Manto was born in 1912, into a middle-class Kashmiri family of Amritsar, India. In 1936 he went to Delhi to edit a weekly film magazine, and in 1941 he joined the All India Radio. He returned to Bombay in 1943 to work with a group of friends at the famous Bombay talkies. In January 1948, he moved to Karachi in Pakistan, as life for him as a high profile Muslim in Bombay had become intolerable. He eventually died in 1955, having drunk himself to death.

Farrukh Dhondy

Farrukh Dhondy was born in 1944 in Poona, India. He grew up loving reading, and has written that for him 'Reading was not so much a window on the world as a telescope.' After a fruitless year studying chemical technology, he began to study the classics of literature, and applied for several scholarships overseas. He studied Literature at Cambridge University and directed plays, as well as editing a literary magazine. After gaining his second degree he taught English for several years, and began to write fiction for young adults. His books have received much critical acclaim, and he is famous for his ability to mix humour with harsh reality, often depicting the conflicts that immigrant teenagers in Britain experience. Nicholas Tucker has said that reading Dhondy 'is like going behind the teenage mask and finding the private individual underneath'.

Ravinder Randhawa

Ravinder Randhawa was born in India, but has lived in Britain for most of her life. She has published many short stories and three novels: *A Wicked Old Woman*, *Hari-jan* – a teenage novel and *The Coral Strand*. At the moment she is working on her next novel: *The Snake Charmer's Daughter*. She is a member of PEN International and has recently taken up a Fellowship with the Royal Literary Fund, based at Toynbee Hall.

Paul Wong (now called Paul Wu)

Paul Wong (now Paul Wu) was born in Glasgow, Scotland to Malaysian Chinese and Mauritian Chinese parents. He was brought up in South London, had a 10 year career as a professional dancer and then studied journalism. He has contributed articles, short stories and poetry to many publications and anthologies. He changed his name to Wu when he married, and is currently working as a freelance director/producer primarily for the BBC and Channel 4. He is also writing a serialised novel *The Adventures of Sidekick Shang* for *Brushstrokes* magazine.

Ama Ata Aidoo

Ama Ata Aidoo was born in 1942 in Ghana, Africa, and attended Wesley Girls School, Cape Coast. She graduated from the University of Ghana in 1964, became a research fellow there, and then studied creative writing in California, USA. There she began to write short stories, poetry and plays. She sees her role as revolutionary, fighting for women's rights and self-expression. From 1970 to the early 1980s she was a lecturer at the University of Cape Coast, Ghana, and she has taught and lectured in many countries. She is considered to be Africa's finest living author. She is Brandeis University's Distinguished Visiting Professor and was Ghana's Minister for Education from 1982 to 1983.

THE PEACELIKE MONGOOSE

By James Thurber

Outcomes

Discussion of Issues

What is culture?
Being an outsider
Disobeying the rules
Inclusion/exclusion

Literacy Work

Text Level
Codes and conventions of fable writing
Writing fables

Sentence level
Truisms
Puns
Speech mark paragraphing
Colons

Word level
Word building – prefixes, suffixes, word roots
Abstract nouns

Drama and Oral Activities

Circle of whispers
Rumour mill
Re-enactment

Stimulus Page

Before you begin, find out as much as you can about cobras and mongooses.

This story is a fable – what is a fable?

Study the picture on page 10 – what does it suggest to you?

Is there anything happening in the world today that is similar to this?

The first three words of this story are, 'In cobra country . . .' What images do you have in your mind about what this place might be like?

THE PEACELIKE MONGOOSE

By James Thurber

In cobra country a mongoose was born one day who didn't want to fight cobras or anything else. The word spread from mongoose to mongoose that there was a mongoose who didn't want to fight cobras. If he didn't want to fight anything else, it was his own business, but it was the duty of every mongoose to kill cobras or be killed by cobras.

'Why?' asked the peacelike mongoose, and the word went round that the strange new mongoose was not only pro-cobra and anti-mongoose but intellectually curious and against the ideals and traditions of mongoosism.

'He is crazy,' cried the young mongoose's father.

'He is sick,' said his mother.

'He is a coward,' shouted his brothers.

'He is a mongoosexual,' whispered his sisters.

Strangers who had never laid eyes on the peacelike mongoose remembered that they had seen him crawling on his stomach, or trying on cobra hoods, or plotting the violent overthrow of Mongoosia.

'I am trying to use reason and intelligence,' said the strange new mongoose.

'Reason is six-sevenths of treason,' said one of his neighbours.

'Intelligence is what the enemy uses,' said another.

Finally the rumour spread that the mongoose had venom in his sting, like a cobra, and he was tried, convicted by a show of paws, and condemned to banishment.

Moral: Ashes to ashes, and clay to clay, if the enemy doesn't get you your own folks may.

FRANKIE MAE*

By Jean Wheeler Smith

Outcomes

Discussion of Issues

Racial prejudice and discrimination
Poverty
Civil rights
Cultural pride and self-respect

TB 18   TB 15

Literacy Work

Text Level
Studying the lives of the characters
Structuring stories: flashback
Point of view
Writing: catalogue of injustice
       school work, Frankie Mae's story
       composing a speech

TB 15

TB 18   TB 17   TB 18

Word Level
Creating a voice: adapting spelling and grammar

TB 16

Drama and Oral Activities

Role play: the Civil Rights meeting
Voices round: at the graveside; round the family table
Tableaux

TB 18

*Please note these stories contain strong language.

Stimulus Page

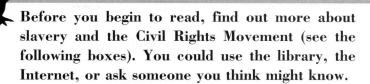

Before you begin to read, find out more about slavery and the Civil Rights Movement (see the following boxes). You could use the library, the Internet, or ask someone you think might know.

Start by finding out as much as you can about slavery and its effect on the lives of people of different races in the United States of America.

You could then find out more about the Civil Rights Movement that was active when this story was first published in 1968. What did they campaign for?

'It's not fair!' We often use or hear this phrase, but what examples of real injustice are there in the world do you think? What would you campaign for?

Although this story is called *Frankie Mae*, it begins with her father, waiting outside the gate of the White Plantation. This time he is not waiting meekly for work . . .

FRANKIE MAE

By *Jean Wheeler Smith*

The sun had just started coming up when the men gathered at the gate of the White Plantation. They leaned on the fence, waiting. No one was nervous, though. They'd all been waiting a long time. A few more minutes couldn't make much difference. They surveyed the land that they were leaving, the land from which they had brought forth seas of cotton.

Old Man Brown twisted around so that he leaned sideways on the gate. Even though he was in his fifties, he was still a handsome man. Medium-sized, with reddish-brown skin. His beard set him apart from the others; it was the same mixture of black and grey as his hair, but while his hair looked like wool, the strands of his beard were long and nearly straight. He was proud of it, and even when he wasn't able to take a bath, he kept his beard neatly cut and shaped into a V.

He closed his eyes. The sun was getting too bright; it made his headache worse. 'Damn,' he thought, 'I sure wouldn't be out here this early on no Monday morning if it wasn't for what we got to do today. Whisky'll sure kill you if you don't get some sleep long with it. I wasn't never just crazy 'bout doing this, anyway. Wonder what made me decide to go along?'

Then he smiled to himself. ''Course. It was on account a Frankie Mae. She always getting me into something.'

Frankie was his first child, born twenty-two years ago, during the war. When she was little, she had gone everywhere with him. He had a blue bicycle with a rusty wire basket in the front. He used to put Frankie Mae in the basket and ride her to town with him and to the café, and sometimes they'd go nowhere special, just riding. She'd sit sideways so that she could see what was on the road ahead and talk with him at the same time. She never bothered to hold onto the basket; she knew her daddy wouldn't let her fall. Frankie fitted so well into the basket that for a few years the Old Man thought that it was growing with her.

She was a black child, with huge green eyes that seemed to glow in the dark. From the age of four on she had a look of being full-grown. The look was in her muscular, well-defined limbs that seemed like they could do a woman's work and in her way of seeing everything around her. Most times she was alive and happy. The only thing wrong with her was that she got hurt so easy. The slightest rebuke sent her crying; the least hint of disapproval left her moody and depressed for hours. But on the other side of it was that she had a way of springing back from pain. No matter how hurt she had been, she would be her old self by the next day. The Old Man worried over her. He wanted most to cushion her life.

When Frankie reached six, she became too large to ride in the basket with him. Also he had four more children by then. So he bought a car for forty dollars. Not long afterwards he became restless. He'd heard about how you could make a lot of money over in the delta. So he decided to go over there. He packed what he could carry in one load – the children, a few chickens, and a mattress – and slipped off one night.

Two days after they left the hills, they drove up to the White Plantation in Loflore County, Mississippi. They were given a two-room house that leaned to one side and five dollars to make some groceries with for the next month.

The Old Man and his wife, Mattie, worked hard that year. Up at four-thirty and out to the field. Frankie Mae stayed behind to nurse the other children and to watch the pot that was cooking for dinner. At sundown they came back home and got ready for the next day. They did a little sweeping, snapped some beans for dinner the next day, and washed for the baby. Then they sat on the porch together for maybe a half hour.

That was the time the Old Man liked best, the half hour

before bed. He and Frankie talked about what had happened during the day, and he assured her that she had done a good job keeping up the house. Then he went on about how smart she was going to be when she started school. It would be in two years, when the oldest boy was big enough to take care of the others.

One evening on the porch Frankie said, 'A man from town come by today looking for our stove. You know the short one, the one ain't got no hair. Said we was three weeks behind and he was gonna take it. Had a truck to take it back in, too.'

The Old Man lowered his head. He was ashamed that Frankie had had to face that man by herself. No telling what he said to her. And she took everything so serious. He'd have to start teaching her how to deal with folks like that.

'What did you tell him, baby?' he asked. 'He didn't hurt you none, did he?'

'No, he didn't bother me, sides looking mean. I told him I just this morning seen some money come in the mail from Uncle Ed in Chicago. And I heard my daddy say he was gonna use it to pay off the stoveman. So he said "Well, I give y'all one more week, one more." And he left.'

The Old Man pulled Frankie to him and hugged her. 'You did 'zactly right, honey.' She understood. She would be able to take care of herself.

The end of the first year in the delta the Old Man and Mattie went to settle up. It was just before Christmas. When their turn came, they were called by Mr White Junior, a short fat man, with a big stomach, whose clothes were always too tight.

'Let me see, Johnnie,' he said. 'Here it is. You owe two hundred dollars.'

The Old Man was surprised. Sounded just like he was back in the hills. He had expected things to be different over here. He had made a good crop. Should have cleared something. Well, no sense in arguing. The bossman counted out fifty dollars.

'Here's you some Christmas money,' Mr White Junior said. 'Pay me when you settle up next year.'

The Old Man took the money to town that same day and bought himself some barrels and some pipes and a bag of chopped corn. He had made whisky in the hills, and he could make it over here, too. You could always find somebody to buy it. Wasn't no reason he should spend all his time farming if he couldn't make nothing out of it. He and Mattie put up their barrels in the trees down by the river and set their mash to ferment.

By spring Brown had a good business going. He sold to the coloured cafés and even to some of the white ones. And folks knew they could always come to his house if they ran out. He didn't keep the whisky at the house, though. Too dangerous, it was buried down by the water. When folks came unexpected, it was up to Frankie and her brother next to her to go get the bottles. Nobody noticed children. The Old Man bought them a new red wagon for their job.

He was able to pay off his stove and give Mattie some money every once in a while. And they ate a little better now. But still they didn't have much more than before because Brown wasn't the kind of man to save. Also he had to do a lot of drinking himself to keep up his sales. Folks didn't like to drink by themselves. When he'd start to drinking, he usually spent up or gave away whatever he had in his pocket. So they still had to work as hard as ever for Mr White Junior. Brown enjoyed selling the whisky, though, and Mattie could always go out and sell a few bottles in case of some emergency like their lights being cut off. So they kept the business going.

That spring Mr White Junior decided to take them off shares. He would pay one dollar fifty a day for chopping cotton, and he'd pay by the hundred pound for picking. The hands had no choice. They could work by the day or leave. Actually, the Old Man liked it better working by the day. Then he would have more time to see to his whisky.

Also, Mr White Junior made Brown the timekeeper over the other hands. Everybody had drunk liquor with him, and most folks liked him. He could probably keep them working better than anybody else. He did fight too much. But the hands knew that he always carried his pistol. If anybody fought him, they'd have to be trying to kill him, 'cause he'd be trying to kill them.

Brown was given a large, battered watch. So he'd know what time to stop for dinner. His job was to see that the hands made a full day in the field and that all the weeds got chopped.

The job was easier than getting out there chopping in all that sun. So Brown liked it. The only hard part was in keeping after the women whose time was about to come. He hated to see them dragging to the field, their bellies about to burst. They were supposed to keep up with the others, which was impossible. Oftentimes Mr White Junior slipped up on the work crew and found one of the big-bellied women lagging behind the others.

'Goddamit, Johnnie,' he'd say, 'I done told you to keep the hands together. Queenester is way behind. I don't pay good money for folks to be standing around. If she sick, she need to go home.'

Sometimes the Old Man felt like defending the woman. She had done the best she could. But then he'd think, No, better leave things like they is.

'You sure right, Mr White Junior. I was just 'bout to send her home myself. Some niggers too lazy to live.'

He would walk slowly across the field to the woman. 'I'm sorry, Queenester. The bossman done seen you. I told you all to be looking out for him! Now you got to go. You come back tomorrow, though. He won't hardly be back in this field so soon. I try and let you make two more days this week. I know you needs the little change.'

The woman would take up her hoe and start walking home. Mr White Junior didn't carry no hands except to eat dinner and to go home after the day had been made.

One day when he had carried the hands in from the field, Mr White Junior stopped the Old Man as he was climbing down from the back of the pick-up truck. While the bossman talked, Brown fingered his timekeeper's watch that hung on a chain from his belt.

'Johnnie,' Mr White Junior said, 'It don't look right to me for you to leave a girl at home that could be working when I need all the hands I can get. And you the timekeeper, too. This cotton can't wait on you all to get ready to chop it. I want Frankie Mae out there tomorrow.'

He had tried to resist. 'But we getting along with what me and Mattie makes. Ain't got nothing, but we eating. I wants Frankie Mae to go to school. We can do without the few dollars she would make.'

'I want my cotton chopped,' White said, swinging his fat

sweating body into the truck. 'Get that girl down here tomorrow. Don't nobody stay in my house and don't work.'

That night the Old Man dreaded the half hour on the porch. When Frankie had started school that year, she had already been two years late. And she had been so excited about going.

When the wood had been gathered and the children cleaned up, he followed Frankie onto the sloping porch. She fell to telling him about the magnificent yellow bus in which she rode to school. He sat down next to her on the step.

'Frankie Mae, I'm going to tell you something.'

'What's that, Daddy? Mamma say I been slow 'bout helping 'round the house since I been going to school? I do better. Guess I lost my head.'

'No, baby. That ain't it at all. You been helping your Mama fine.' He stood up to face her but could not bring his eyes to the level of her bright, happy face.

'Mr White Junior stopped me today when I was getting off the truck. Say he want you to come to field till the chopping get done.'

She found his eyes. 'What did you say, Daddy?'

'Well, I told him you wanted to go to school, and we could do without your little money. But he say you got to go.'

The child's eyes lost their brilliance. Her shoulders slumped, and she began to cry softly. Tired, the Old Man sat back down on the step. He took her hand and sat with her until long after Mattie and the other children had gone to bed.

The next morning Frankie was up first. She put on two blouses and a dress and some pants to keep off the sun and found herself a rag to tie around her head. Then she woke up her daddy and the others, scolding them for being so slow.

'We got to go get all that cotton chopped! And y'all laying round wasting good daylight. Come on.'

Brown got up and threw some water on his face. He saw Frankie bustling around in her layers of clothes, looking like a little old woman, and he smiled. That's how Frankie Mae was. She'd feel real bad, terrible for a few hours, but she always snapped back. She'd be all right now.

On the way to the field he said, 'Baby, I'm gonna make you the water girl. All you got to do is carry water over to them that hollers for it and keep your bucket full. You don't have to chop none lest you see Mr White Junior coming.'

'No, Daddy, that's all right. The other hands'll say you was letting me off easy 'cause I'm yours. Say you taking advantage of being timekeeper. I go on and chop with the rest.'

He tried to argue with her, but she wouldn't let him give her the water bucket. Finally he put her next to Mattie so she could learn from her. As he watched over the field, he set himself not to think about his child inhaling the cotton dust and insecticide. When his eyes happened on her and Mattie, their backs bent way over, he quickly averted them. Once, when he jerked his eyes away, he found instead the bright yellow school bus bouncing along the road.

Frankie learned quickly how to chop the cotton, and sometimes she even seemed to enjoy herself. Often the choppers would go to the store to buy sardines and crackers and beans for their dinner instead of going home. At the store the Old Man would eat his beans from their jagged-edge can and watch with pride as Frankie laughed and talked with everyone and made dates with the ladies to attend church on the different plantations. Every Sunday Frankie had a service to go to. Sometimes, when his head wasn't bad from drinking, the Old Man went with her because he liked so much to see her enjoy herself. Those times he put a few gallons of his whisky in the back of the car just in case somebody needed them. When he and Frankie went off to church like that, they didn't usually get back till late at night. They would be done sold all the whisky and the Old Man would be talking loud about the wonderful sermon that the reverend had preached and all the souls that had come to Jesus.

That year they finished the chopping in June. It was too late to send Frankie back to school, and she couldn't go again until after the cotton had been picked. When she went back in November she had missed four months and found it hard to keep up with the children who'd been going all the time. Still, she went every day that she could. She stayed home only when she had to, when her mother was sick or when, in the cold weather, she didn't have shoes to wear.

Whenever she learned that she couldn't go to school on a particular day, she withdrew into herself for about an hour. She had a chair near the stove, where she sat, and the little children knew not to bother her. After the hour she'd push back her chair and go to stirring the cotton in the bed ticks or washing the greens for dinner.

If this was possible, the Old Man loved her still more now. He saw the children of the other workers and his own children, too, get discouraged and stop going to school. They said it was too confusing; they never knew what the teacher was talking about because they'd not been there the day before or the month before. And they resented being left behind in classes with children half their size. He saw the other children get so that they wouldn't hold themselves up, wouldn't try to be clean and make folks respect them. Yet every other day Frankie managed to put on a clean starched dress, and she kept at her lessons.

By the time Frankie was thirteen she could figure as well as the preacher, and she was made secretary of the church.

That same year she asked her daddy if she could keep a record of what they made and what they spent.

'Sure, baby,' he said. 'I'll be proud for you to do it. We might even come out a little better this year when we settle up. I tell you what. If we get some money outta Mr White Junior this year, I'll buy you a dress for Christmas, a red one.'

Frankie bought a black-and-white-speckled notebook. She put in it what they made and what they paid on their bill. After chopping time she became excited. She figured they had just about paid the bill out. What they made from picking should be theirs. She and the Old Man would sit on the porch and go over the figures and plan for Christmas. Sometimes they even talked about taking a drive up to Chicago to see Uncle Ed. Every so often he would try to hold down her excitement by reminding her that their figures had to be checked against the bossman's. Actually, he didn't expect to do much better than he'd done all the other years. But she was so proud to be using what she had learned, her numbers and all. He hated to discourage her.

Just before Christmas they went to settle up. When it came to the Old Man's turn, he trembled a little. He knew it was almost too much to hope for, that they would have money coming to them. But some of Frankie's excitement had rubbed off on him.

He motioned to her, and they went up to the table where there were several stacks of ten and twenty dollar bills, a big ledger, and a pistol. Mr White Junior sat in a brown chair, and his agent stood behind him. Brown took heart from the absolute confidence with which Frankie Mae walked next to him, and he controlled his trembling. Maybe the child was right and they had something coming to them.

'Hey there, Johnnie,' Mr White Junior said, 'see you brought Frankie Mae along. Fine, fine. Good to start them early. Here's you a seat.'

The Old Man gave Frankie the one chair and stood beside her. The bossman rifled his papers and came out with a long narrow sheet. Brown recognized his name at the top.

'Here you are, Johnnie, y'all come out pretty good this year. Proud of you. Don't owe but $65. Since you done so good, gonna let you have $100 for Christmas.'

Frankie Mae spoke up. 'I been keeping a book for my daddy. And I got some different figures. Let me show you.'

The room was still. Everyone, while pretending not to notice the girl, was listening intently to what she said.

Mr White Junior looked surprised, but he recovered quickly.

'Why sure. Be glad to look at your figures. You know it's easy to make a mistake. I'll show you what you done wrong.'

Brown clutched her shoulder to stop her from handing over the book. But it was too late. Already she was leaning over the table, comparing her figures with those in the ledger.

'See, Mr White Junior, when we was chopping last year we made $576, and you took $320 of that to put on our bill. There. There it is on your book. And we borrowed $35 in July. There it is . . .'

The man behind the table grew red. One of his fat hands gripped the table while the other moved toward the pistol.

Frankie Mae finished. 'So you see, you owe us $180 for the year.'

The bossman stood up to gain the advantage of his height. He seemed about to burst. His eyes flashed around the room, and his hand clutched the pistol. He was just raising it from the table when he caught hold of himself. He took a deep breath and let go of the gun.

'Oh, yeah. I remember what happened now, Johnnie. It was that slip I gave to the doctor for Willie B. You remember, last year, 'fore chopping time. I got the bill last week. Ain't had time to put it in my book. It came to, let me think. Yeah, that was $350.

The Old Man's tension fell away from him, and he resumed his normal manner. He knew exactly what the bossman was saying. It was as he had expected, as it had always been.

'Let's go, baby,' he said.

But Frankie didn't get up from the chair. For a moment she looked puzzled. Then her face cleared. She said, 'Willie didn't have anything wrong with him but a broken arm. The doctor spent twenty minutes with him one time and ten minutes the other. That couldn't cost no $350!'

The bossman's hand found the pistol again and gripped it until the knuckles were white. Brown pulled Frankie to him and put his arm around her. With his free hand he fingered his own pistol, which he always carried in his pocket. He was not afraid. But he hated the thought of shooting the man; even if he just nicked him, it would be the end for himself. He drew a line: If Mr White Junior touched him or Frankie, he would shoot. Short of that he would leave without a fight.

White spat thick, brown tobacco juice onto the floor, spattering it on the Old Man and the girl. 'Nigger,' he said, 'I know you ain't disputing my word. Don't nobody live on my place and call me no liar. That bill was $350. You understand me?' He stood tense, staring with hatred at the man and the girl. Everyone waited for Brown's answer. The Old Man felt Frankie's arms go 'round his waist.

'Tell him no, Daddy. We right, not him. I kept them figures all year, they got to be right.' The gates of the state farm flashed through the Old Man's mind. He thought of Mattie, already sick from high blood, trying to make a living for eleven people. Frankie's arms tightened.

'Yessir,' he said. 'I understand.'

The girl's arms dropped from him, and she started to the door. The other workers turned away to fiddle with a piece of rope, to scold a child. Brown accepted the $50 that was thrown across the table to him. As he turned to follow Frankie, he heard Mr White Junior's voice, low now and with a controlled violence. 'Hey you, girl. You, Frankie Mae.' She stopped at the door but didn't turn around.

'Long as you live, bitch, I'm gonna be right and you gonna be wrong. Now get your black ass outta here.'

Frankie stumbled out to the car and crawled onto the back seat. She cried all the way home. Brown tried to quiet her. She could still have the red dress. They'd go down to the river tomorrow and start on a new batch of whisky.

The next morning he laid in bed waiting to hear Frankie Mae

moving around and fussing, waiting to know that she had snapped back to her old self. He laid there until everyone in the house had gotten up. Still he did not hear her. Finally he got up and went over to where she was balled up in the quilts.

He woke her. 'Come on, baby. Time to get up. School bus be here soon.'

'I ain't goin' today,' she said, 'got a stomach ache.'

Brown sat out on the porch all day long, wishing that she would get up out the bed and struggling to understand what had happened. This time Frankie had not bounced back to her old bright-eyed self. The line that held her to this self had been stretched too taut. It had lost its tension and couldn't pull her back.

Frankie never again kept a book for her daddy. She lost interest in things such as numbers and reading. She went to school as an escape from chores but got so little of her lessons done that she was never promoted from the fourth grade to the fifth. When she was fifteen and in the fourth grade, she had her first child. After that there was no more thought of school. In the following four years she had three more children.

She sat around the house, eating and growing fat. When well enough, she went to the field with her daddy. Her dresses were seldom ironed now. Whatever she could find to wear would do.

Still there were a few times, maybe once every three or four months, when she was lively and fresh. She'd get dressed and clean the children up and have her daddy drive them to church. On such days she'd be the first one up. She would have food on the stove before anybody else had a chance to dress. Brown would load up his trunk with whisky, and they'd stay all day.

It was for these isolated times that the Old Man waited. They kept him believing that she would get to be all right. Until she died, he woke up every morning listening for her laughter, waiting for her to pull the covers from his feet and scold him for being lazy.

She died giving birth to her fifth child. The midwife, Esther, was good enough, but she didn't know what to do when there were complications. Brown couldn't get up but $60 of the $100 cash that you had to deposit at the county hospital. So they wouldn't let Frankie in. She bled to death on the hundred-mile drive to the charity hospital in Vicksburg.

The Old Man squinted up at the fully risen sun. The bossman

was late. Should have been at the gate by now. Well, it didn't matter. Just a few more minutes and they'd be through with the place forever.

His thoughts went back to the time when the civil rights workers had first come around and they had started their meetings up at the store. They'd talked about voting and about how plantation workers should be making enough to live off. Brown and the other men had listened and talked and agreed. So they decided to ask Mr White Junior for a raise. They wanted nine dollars for their twelve-hour day.

They had asked. And he had said, Hell no. Before he'd raise them he'd lower them. So they agreed to ask him again. And if he still said no, they would go on strike.

At first Brown hadn't understood himself why he agreed to the strike. It was only this morning that he realised why: It wasn't the wages or the house that was falling down 'round him and Mattie. It was that time when he went to ask Mr White Junior about the other $40 that he needed to put Frankie in the hospital.

'Sorry, Johnnieboy,' he'd said, patting Brown on the back, 'but me and Miz White having a garden party today and I'm so busy. You know how women are. She want me there every minute. See me tomorrow. I'll fix you up then.'

A cloud of dust rose up in front of Brown. The bossman was barrelling down the road in his pick-up truck. He was mad. That was what he did when he got mad, drove his truck up and down the road fast. Brown chuckled. When they got through with him this morning, he might run that truck into the river.

Mr White Junior climbed down from the truck and made his way over to the gate. He began to give the orders for the day, who would drive the tractors, what fields would be chopped. The twelve men moved away from the fence, disdaining any support for what they were about to do.

One of the younger ones, James Lee, spoke up. 'Mr White Junior, we wants to know is you gonna raise us like we asked?'

'No, goddammit. Now go on, do what I told you.'

'Then,' James Lee continued, 'we got to go on strike from this place.'

James Lee and the others left the gate and went to have a strategy meeting up at the store about what to do next.

The Old Man was a little behind the rest because he had something to give Mr White Junior. He went over the sweat-drenched, cursing figure and handed him the scarred timekeeper's watch, the watch that had ticked away Frankie Mae's youth in the hot, endless rows of cotton.

INVISIBLE MASS OF THE BACK ROW

By *Claudette Williams*

Outcomes

Discussion of Issues

Cultural heritage – its importance
Knowledge is power
What changes people? – changing countries,
changing viewpoints

TB 22

Literacy Work

Text Level
Character analysis
Poetry – analysis and annotation
What makes a good short story?

Word level
Adding detail – adjectives and nouns

TB 20 TB 21
TB 22 TB 25
TB 23 TB 24

Drama and Oral Activities

Hot-seating characters from the story
Reading the story as a playscript

Stimulus Page

Before you begin this story, make sure you know something about the setting of the first part of the story: Jamaica. Find out as much as you can about Jamaica, its history and people.

It will also be useful to understand more about Christopher Columbus and the effects of his voyages on the Caribbean islands.

Now look carefully at the title of this story. What does it mean to you? Do you have any experience of being in this position yourself?

You will find some interesting contrasts in this story, particularly in the way that the places are described. Look out for the way the writer uses description.

This story is written in the first person: 'I stand in the middle of the room . . .' Why do you think the writer chose to write as if Hortense was actually telling her own story?

INVISIBLE MASS OF THE BACK ROW

By Claudette Williams

I stand in the middle of the room, surrounded by anxious faces. It is my turn to recite the day's lesson. The Inspector's ruler points to me.

'Stand up. Recite the adventures of Columbus. What was the date of Columbus' landing in Jamaica? What were the names of his ships? Why was he in the Caribbean?'

My heart pounds. The heat of the morning sun, soaking through the galvanised roof, is magnified inside the schoolroom. The stench of fear is in everyone's nostrils. Something tells me that my days of being hidden, disposed of, dispatched to the invisibility of the back row, are numbered.

I stand up, my limbs shaking uncontrollably, sweat dripping from my armpits, my eyes inflamed. My belly aches. I am petrified. Words fail to come out. They are formed in my head, but my lips do not speak them. The Inspector's eyes pierce me through. They demand a response, demand to be respected and obeyed.

'What was Columbus doing here anyway?' The trapped words inside my head tumble out. The rebel inside me is alive. The schoolroom becomes even quieter, if that is possible.

'You in for it,' Patricia, sitting next to where I stand shaking, mutters without moving her lips. I know she is speaking the truth.

The Inspector's face is frozen. Miss Henderson, form six teacher, pounces with the ruler. Her face says she is sure she could not have heard what she thought she heard.

'What did you say, Hortense?'

From I don't know where, a power surges through me. My fists clench. My teeth lock into each other. Miss Henderson reads challenge in my face. I stand still, not daring to say any more.

'What did you say?' she commands, challenging me to repeat my *facetiness*. And again it happens. Words gush out of my mouth. 'Is what Columbus did want? Who invite him here?'

Before the last word has left my lips, the sharp sting of the ruler cracks my knuckles. Stupidly, I had left my clenched fist on the desk in front of me. The blow brings me back to the steam bath. Sweat now drips from my face, floods my armpits, drips from between my legs.

I could kill this woman with her sharp pointed nose, mean eyes and frightened face. We cross eyes, and for an instant I see the fear which has trapped us in this rank, smelly room. Miss Henderson is afraid. She is as much afraid of the Inspector as I am.

My brains, what brains I have left, are bouncing around in my skull, goading me on. I will get more of the ruler. It is written across Miss Henderson's wrinkled forehead. My life is at an end! At least in this school. If Miss Henderson does not kill me with this ruler, my aunt is sure to finish me off when she hears how I back-chat the Inspector and Teacher Henderson.

My parents are in England and living with my aunt is like walking a tight-rope. One little slip and I am in big trouble. Dis look and smell like big trouble to me.

The lunch bell echoes throughout the school. My salvation? For now, anyway.

Hungry bellies rumble in the steam bath, but we are still transfixed by the Inspector, paralysed by Miss Henderson's stare. Feet shuffle, fingers scratch prickly skin. From outside there is the freedom of released bodies bouncing against the partition and liberated voices rising. They magnify our imprisonment. But the walls have been breached. The jailers are quick to realise that this battle is lost. For now.

'Class dismissed,' the Inspector grudgingly commands. Miss Henderson lowers her eyes.

'Good afternoon, Inspector. Good afternoon, Miss Henderson,' we recite. Miss Henderson steps aside, stiffly. Fifty tense bodies scurry past, politely, straining to taste the fresh, if hot air of the noon-day world and feed themselves from the lunch women under the cotton tree. But first there is Lorna Phillips to take care of. Somebody has to pay for this.

'Yo red pickney always sit a de front of de class. Unno t'ink is because yu pretty. Is only 'cause teacher frighten fi yu pupa,' I curse Lorna, as we bundle down the steps, out of earshot of Miss Henderson and the Inspector.

'Is 'cause yu black and stupid why teacher meck yu sit a de back all de time,' Lorna chirps in.

'Is who you calling stupid? Yo want yu bloody nose right here?'

This is always the outcome of a tense morning in school. A fight often follows the Inspector's visits.

Lorna pushes past me and tries to make a break for the school gate. But I give chase, followed by Samuel, Tim, Patricia, Maud and Yvonne. Today she will pay for being teacher's favourite, for being 'red', for being rich, for having everything I don't have.

'Look how fast she moving on dem marga foot,' taunts Yvonne.

'Come, let we beat her up,' I shout, and we surge forward, pursuing Lorna out of school.

I might not know the answers, but I can fight.

Just then, from behind the school gate, Teacher Edwards comes into view. He is big, sturdy and beautifully dark, with a baby moustache. He is handsomely dressed in his Dashiki suit. There is a kindness about this man that is not usually found among teachers. He would always listen to you, and not just take the teacher's side. He only beat you if he really feel you was out of order, rude, or you get catch with something you thief. We respected and even liked him.

The running stops, slows to a polite walk. The hot pursuit melts into fixed grins and prim steps.

'Good afternoon, children.'

'Good afternoon, Teacher Edwards,' we still the vengeance in our voices long enough to chant in unison.

Lorna makes the most of Teacher Edwards' presence.

Walking as fast as she could, she says her polite good afternoon and makes a beeline for the hill which distances her from the rest of us. She is safe this time. We turn down the hill. 'Meck she gone. We'll get her tomorrow,' we plot. My voice and limbs quiet down. For the first time that day, my heartbeat falls back into its normal silent rhythm. There is always tomorrow.

It is the pain of the Inspector that has fuelled my blood; the pain of the ruler was nothing. Chu, mi use to beatings. One little ruler slap a nothing. But dat renking, facety man. A way him come from? Dis warra warra man, jus' a bother people head. Him 'now de score. After all him is suppose to be black.

My uncle say all a dem collude to humiliate, not just me, but all a we, all de people who look like me. All de poor black people dem. Meck him no pick pan de red pickney dem, a meck him t'ink say is we alone no know nothing.

I walk silently down the hill with the others. Each of us is distracted by our own thoughts and anger at the morning. Food hunger is temporarily forgotten. Lorna Phillips and de Inspector dem all de same. Have plenty of money and hate we.

At the bottom of the hill, we are nourished by a wealth of warm, familiar sights and smells. The lunch women come into view. They are always there, big and strong, jutting out from the base of the towering cotton tree. Miss Ivy, as always, has on her red tie-head. In the afternoon sun, as she sits on her three-legged stool, it makes her face glow. Her food box is secured between her legs.

Aunt Dine always smells of cinnamon. You know her smell, because if you dare to make her laugh and expose her bare toothless black gums, in quiet moments she will give you a big smothering hug. Her missing teeth give her face a funny, quaint look. She is never scary to us because she lives in our district and we know her.

Miss Mavis always sits to the right of Aunt Dine, because, she says, she is practising to be on the right hand side of her Maker. Miss Mavis has the most beautifully oiled, ivory coloured skin in the whole world, and white, white eyes which twinkle and wink at you when she talks. She is never cross for long, but will cuss you out one minute and tell you scriptures the next. Her face is electric, whirling and changing as she speaks. Her eyes search your face for understanding.

And then there is one-foot Herby who is always late with his sky-juice and snowball. He can argue, always on about 'de dam hot sun,' which is, 'good for nothing, and only melting him ice, quick, quick, o'clock.'

The boxes are unwrapped. Our senses are assaulted by saltfish fritters, fried dumplings, red herring, cornmeal pudding, sweet potato pudding, oranges, plums, mangoes or sugar-cane, snowball and sky-juice. Smells mingle and whirl, creating a comfortable oasis under the gigantic cotton tree. That same tree serves as a lover's nest and gambling spot at nights. If trees could talk, what stories this one would tell!

We go down the hill. The gloom of humiliation, the pain of the assault on all of us, lifts. We search for our lunch money and think of food. Like swarming bees we descend, shouting our orders to the lunch women.

'Unny stop de noise and wait. How many han' yu t'ink we have?' Miss Mavis quietly reprimands.

The shouts subside only for a moment as we change our orders and surge again.

'Two penny worth of dumpling and saltfish, please Miss Mavis.'

'Mi only want fritters.'

'Mi jus' want a piece of cornmeal pudding today.'

'But Aunt Dine dat red herring so little bit.'

'Yu have no crackers again Miss Ivy?'

'How come Herby teck so long fi share de ice?'

The clutter and bustle carry on until the sweat is running down the women's faces. Wash-rags, carried on shoulders like a uniform, mop brows, as they try to keep track of orders and change.

'Lord unny pickney is somet'ing else. Unny gone like nobody no feed unny. Dem mus' a wok unny hard a school today.'

The chatter waves and heaves. The banter and retort goes backwards and forwards until the lunch money secured in pockets and knotted in handkerchiefs has been spent for the day.

Boxes are empty. We mingle, swap and taste each other's purchases, eat, talk with mouths full. As we drift away, so do Aunt Mavis, Aunt Dine and Miss Ivy. Herby is the last to pack up and vacate the cotton tree. The forces have been spent for the day.

Will I one day move from the back row? Would I be let off from reciting the day's lesson, because I know it, just once?

Would it ever be my turn to sit at the front, and not have to answer the Inspector's questions?

The house is buzzing. A letter and a big, big parcel have arrived from England. 'Me mother sending for we. Me and me two brothers going to England.' I sang, 'Me a go a Englan'. Me mumma and puppa send fi we.' Dat will show Lorna Phillips. She have no people in a Englan'. Columbus can get lost. No more standing up in the middle of the class. No more hot, sweaty classroom. No more Teacher Henderson. No more Inspector. Me a go a Englan'.

November sixteenth. It is dark outside. Night creatures are going to sleep. Day animals still don't know it is time to wake up. Inside, the lamp is lit, casting its honey glow on our faces still dazed with sleep.

'Unno go wash, and put on unno clothes,' Salna orders. Sleepily, we obey.

The sun is creeping over Easington hills, reflecting the honey glow inside. Its full power is still waiting to wake up. I cannot drink any tea, cannot eat what is to be my last piece of hard-dough bread and butter. My stomach is tight. My jaws are refusing to chew on this familiar taste.

'If yu don't want de tea, lef' it an go put on yu clothes. Dem all dey pon de chair, and don't mess up de hair,' I am ordered again. I do as I am told. No time for back-chatting.

Now there is much coming and going. In the dim light of morning, not yet fully awake, neighbours come to say farewell. They bring parting gifts of mangoes, and presents for relatives in England, not seen or heard from in many years.

Like a stranger, I greet my new clothes, gingerly feeling, inhaling the new cloth smells. I try to work out which piece to put on first without disturbing my newly crafted hairstyle.

I dress in silence, only now beginning to fully realize. Today, my every action, in this dim morning light, is to be registered in the cosmos as my last in this familiar, tiny, two-roomed house.

We pile into the van just as the morning sun claims its place in the sky. It releases its passions and burns away the last stillness of the night. The silence of parting quiets the most active tongue. The drive to the airport is long and hot. Still, the pain of parting traps us in our silent world.

Who will look after Cousy's grave? Who will make sure that the weeds do not choke her roses?

Cousy had not moved, as she always did, when the sun peeped over the hill top. Had not roused me to do my morning chores when night kiss morning awake. I thought Cousy's coldness was just the passing of night. So I slept on, not noticing that her 'old bones', as she often referred to herself, had not stirred, that her limbs were stiff, that she got colder as the morning got warmer. Lloyd banging on the door, ordering me to get up and feed de chickens, alerted the yard. I woke to find Cousy's gentle face tight and still, a trickle of tears running from her opened eyes.

'Why are you crying Cousy?' I asked as I crept sleepily out of bed. There was no reply. And I found myself crying too. Her stillness, her unfocused stare, signalled a change.

I opened the door to find the whole yard gathered outside, waiting. They understood the signals. Death had crept under the door and taken Cousy away in her sleep.

'I want Cousy,' I hollered, as I fell into Miss Olive's arms.

Does this mean I won't ever again share Cousy's bed and snuggle into her warm bosom? Won't smell her old mysterious smells, and watch her crinkled face?

Now, this thought forces out the hot salty tears which well up inside. I am leaving her behind. The tears flow freely, soiling my newly polished face. Bringing me back to the speeding van taking me away from Heartease, from Cousy, from my goats, from Lorna Phillips. Towards . . . the gigantic, shimmering aeroplanes.

The sun releases all its enormous strength. The sea retaliates. It shimmers its bluest blue, a blue that envelops the airport and the parked aeroplanes.

The following hours are filled with a numbness. The only parallels I can think of are visits to the dentist with anaesthetic injected to deaden the pain or when you freshly buck your toe on a big rock stone. My inside is dead. I am cold in the blazing sunshine.

Now, everybody is crying, some pretending that they aren't. Handkerchiefs flap goodbye and wipe streaming eyes. My brothers and I are ceremoniously handed over to a pretty, chocolate-coloured woman dressed in a blue uniform. We follow her, reluctantly, into places of strangeness, places with strange lights and strange demands. People smile knowingly and gather up our belongings.

Then we are sitting in the belly of the gigantic metal bird, which we have only seen before from the ground, looking upwards. This is it. We are going to England.

England brings my mother and father back to me. It drags them forward from the fragile recesses of my young memory. I remember snippets of incidents which had told me of their existence. How long have we been separated? Well, it is hard to know. It was hard, those days long ago, to understand what was going on. I cannot count how many days I was without my father's company, nor am I positive of the many years without my mother's embrace. But memory surges suggest seven years, perhaps, without father and five without mother.

I was not to know then, that although I would return many times, that first departure was the beginning of my exile from Heartease.

Paraffin heaters
smell
always just coming
into cold dark places
afraid and
excited at the same
time
cold
smell
wanting to be elsewhere
in fact Jamaica

'Yes, Salna,' I replied for the tenth time, to my mother's call from the kitchen. A pokey, steamy place at the back of a cold, cold house.

All the houses I see are stuck together, with no place to play outside, no yard. Do children not play outside in this England? Is it always so cold? Does it ever get warm? Does the sun shine here?

'Now, listen to me child,' my mother's dark, youthful face smiles down at me, brings me back to the steamy place. I sit huddled in strange clothes, close to the paraffin heater. 'You had better decide what you are going to call me. You can choose from Mother, Mummy, Mum. The same goes for your father. You've got Dad, Daddy or Father to choose from.'

This little talk put an end to days of nervous tension about deciding what to call my England parents. Having arrived, what do you call these newly acquired people? I dreaded answering to my mother's call. What do you answer when strangers call to you, but they are not strangers really, they are your mother and father? I fell back on old responses, familiar language.

No one told me I would need a new language in dis England.

'My mother who dey a England; my mother who a send fa me in a England.' Here I was without a language to reply to her calls. Lorna Phillips, I still hate you, but oh I wish you were here. At least I know your name.

Mum came with me for my interview at Devon Spencer School. She sat right next to me as I read for the Headmistress. I read but did not know the words of this new language, could not read the words of this strange book. I did my best. I read until I was told to stop, being corrected by the Headmistress. The Headmistress was impressed. I was impressed. My Mum was impressed. My impressive reading enrolled me in one five, the hottest, baddest stream in the first year, only second to one six, the remedial stream.

My strategic location in one five has a familiar feel about it. There is no Lorna Phillips. In this group we have all recently arrived, from one island or another but mostly from Jamaica and all poor, clearly black and one rung from the back row, the bottom stream. This is home away from home. I simply settle down to school life and cultivate the culture of the back row. We graduate in hair plaiting, make up and cussing. Our section of the common-room is dominated by the smell of hair pomander, face powder and Woolworth's latest perfume fragrances.

'You know say Columbus enslave de Indian dem fine in the islands. De same one dem who save him life, and help him restock him ships and tell him say him no reach India yet.' Joycelin is feeding us information as she leafs through her latest book, discovered at the local library.

'You lie!' The challenge comes from Fay Green. 'Because is Africans dem enslave and ship to de islands, to slave on sugar plantations, fi make sugar fi white people tea in a England.'

The hair on the back of my neck stands up. The room is suddenly very hot. This man, Columbus keeps coming back to haunt me.

'With all de tea dem drink in dis place, is we still a fi meck sugar fi dem fi sweeten it,' says Joycelin as she continues to leaf through the book, stopping every so often to throw out morsels about the exploits of slavers, life on plantations and the fights slaves and the indigenous Indians waged for their freedom. Conversations weave and heave. We move back and forth between anger, total disbelief and downright outrage.

'Is who write dat book you reading?' 'Cause is foolishness you telling me. I don't believe a word of it,' Fay Green finally bursts out.

Each new piece of information is challenged and questioned. We discover heroes, rebels, guerrilla fighters. They help us assert our right to be. Toussaint L'Ouverture, Sojourner Truth, Nanny, Cudjoe, Paul Bogle. The books tell us they all come from our own back yard. Thoughts of them mingle with the hair oils, face powder, and self-affirmation lessons which claim space in our section of the common-room.

Group humiliation replaces individual humiliation here in England schools. This bottom from remedial class gets the meanest, most feared teachers in the school. Their sole intention seem to be to ensure that we know and keep our place. And Columbus keeps coming up. Today's lesson is to make sure we have learnt the lesson of conquest.

Things mingle and whirl in my mind. Easington heat. Easington sweat. English cold. English ice. Frozen faces, frozen information, frozen places.

'Why did Columbus sail to the Indies in 1493, Hortense?' The frozen face cracks momentarily. 'And while you are thinking of the answer, Fay Green you can be thinking of the commodities which Hawkins traded with the Portuguese of the Gold Coast of Africa.'

Indignantly, the back row comes into its own. 'Columbus was looking for a new route to India, so that when he landed in the Caribbean he was good and lost; he thought he was in India. The people who befriended him were massacred and the rest enslaved to mine gold and cultivate sugar. When they died from diseases Europeans brought to the islands, they were replaced by Africans stolen from the Gold Coast of Africa, Miss.'

I said all of this slowly, so that I would say it well. Some of it came out just as I had read it in a book that one of the others had taken from the local library. Slowly, but quickly, because my head was hot and heavy. I can feel the others in the back row feeling proud. We watch the frozen face thaw out. We watch her eyes travel right along the two rows at the back. We watch a stream of red blood rush from the neck to the top of her head.

Fay Green cannot hold her voice back. 'Hawkins traded trinkets for black African people, who were enslaved and shipped to the Caribbean to slave on sugar plantations, to make sugar for English people's tea, Miss.'

All eyes are on the teacher. The back row is tense, wanting an explosion.

The school pips signal the end of the lesson and class five, unusually dignified, stands up and leaves the room. Miss remains fixed to her chair.

Whoops and slaps are heard down the corridor. The back row claims a victory. 'She won't be asking us those stupid questions again, will she?'

Voices are raised, claiming, proclaiming, learning the new language in dis here England.

DEEPER THAN COLOUR

By Ijeoma Inyama

Outcomes

Discussion of Issues

    Gangs in schools
    Resolving conflict
    Individuals vs. groups

Literacy Work

    Text Level
        Writing own short story
        Story within a story
                                    TB 30 TB 29

    Sentence Level
        Syntax of slang

    Word Level
        Patois   TB 28

Drama and Oral Activities

    Counselling the protagonists TB 27

Stimulus Page

People learn in different ways. Some people like to listen, others prefer to be active or to talk in groups. Do a small survey of people sitting near to you. What are their preferred ways of learning: observing and listening or doing and talking?

Nadine, the main 'voice' in this story, is very critical about her English teacher's plan to make everyone in her class mix by constantly changing the seating plan. Do a quick survey of your classes. In how many classes are you directed to a seat? Are there groups where you have a choice? What are the reasons for the seating policies in these classes? Do you agree with them?

Much of the story is told by Nadine, a fifth form '. . . raga-loving, hardcore jungle gyal', who has a very distinctive way of talking. It is the language of her culture, complete with its own words and phrases. Take a few moments and working with a partner, jot down five or six words and phrases used only by your group. The groups in this class are clearly defined by their musical likes and dislikes. What are your musical 'likes' and which musical groups or trends do you 'dislike'? Share your views and see what range of musical tastes there are in your group.

Similarly, fashion – the clothes you choose to wear, define the cultural group you belong to. Make a short list (or draw a diagram) of the different styles that define the groups in your class. Do this sympathetically; this is not a chance to poke fun at people.

Which would be the explosive pairings in your group? Just quietly think about this before you begin to read.

DEEPER THAN COLOUR

By Ijeoma Inyama

God! Miss Halpern, our English teacher, is well renk! She reckons our class would be *'much more productive'* if we weren't sat with our friends. So she moves us about and makes us sit with people she *knows* we'd never sit with through choice. She's vex me *twice*, man! First of all, you don't expect to get treated like a first year when you're in the *fifth* year – I mean, her idea of a seating arrangement is well antiquated! And secondly, she's taken me from my spars, man! Ever since the second year, I've sat next to Heather Phillips, in front of Antoinette Varley and Takesha Brown. Now barely into the first term of the fifth and we get split up!

'Nadine Charles, I want you to sit next to John Danucci in front of my desk.'

Now she's vexed me four times, no, make that five. Sitting next to Danucci *and* in the front row. I can't believe it! Neither can the rest of the class. *Everyone* knows we're the worst pairing ever.

Let me explain some simple rudimentary classroom psychology, while I grab up my books and cuss my way down the aisle. See, I'm no roughneck, but I love my ragga and jungle . . . like the girls I go round with – Heather, Antoinette and Takesha. So naturally we get friendly with like-minded guys. Horace Batchelor's an example, 'Cept for Horace, the guys ain't true ragamuffins, but they do get a roughneck reputation 'cause

they like ragga. Being Black helps. And if you can run the lyrics
. . . well, you're talking god-like status.

But let me get back to Danucci. He hangs out with the
'trendies'. We call them the *Kiss FM posse*. They're into 'British
soul' and buy their clothes from 'Hyper' – anything that's the
latest t'ing. I mean, if it was thrashing two dustbin lids together,
them lot'd be into that, no danger. So, us lot stick to ourselves,
them lot do likewise – and never the twain shall meet stylee. I
mean, if I went to some roughneck ragga sound dressed like them
freaky deakies – some Barbarella meets and rough up Miss
Marple kind of doo-lah I'd get nuff comments!

It must sound like something out of *West Side Story*, the Jets
versus the Sharks. But it ain't. We don't have gang fights. Just
a mutual understanding that we don't have nothing to do with
each other. And that's why me and Danucci are the worst pairing
Miss Halpern could have made.

A ragga-loving, hardcore jungle *gyal* ain't got nothing decent
to say to a trendy freaky deaky.

At morning break my situation is the focus of the playground
discussion. Horace reckons that Miss Halpern needs '*hormone
treatment*', or a good kick up the backside, or both, for what
she's done. Then he hits on me!

'. . . and don't get no ideas!'

'Yeah, and I'm *really* your girlfriend, ain't I?' I snap.
'Besides, I couldn't go out with no freaky deakster. I'd be too
shamed up to walk down the street with him!'

Horace has asked me out twice and twice I've turned him
down. Truth is, I'd be too shamed up to walk down the street
with *him*! I can't stand the way he's always got to have a comb in
his miserable head – but does he ever use it? Now OK, I wouldn't
get on the cover of *Black Hair & Beauty* (Takesha could easy),
but I could sneak in between. So what makes a guy with no class,
style, the personality of a crusty old pair of Y-fronts and looks
that would make Godzilla a hunk think that I'd be interested in
him? Try and explain that to Horace Batchelor. I've tried, but
he won't listen. He reckons I'm the one for him. God knows why.

Two weeks and six English lessons have passed and I'm still
sitting next to Danucci. I give him dirty looks, run down *Kiss FM*
loud enough for him to hear and make sure my books cover at
least half his desk. He ain't said a word to me. Maybe he's scared

of Horace. But it really annoys me 'cause it's like I'm not there! He shares jokes and raves about the latest rare groove with his trendy pals – and they all sit around me, which I can't stand. And he exchanges loving glances with his girlfriend, Debra Haynes. She sits in the back row, two seats away from Heather. You've got to see this girl. She thinks she's *it*, her nose up in the air or looking down it at you. She's well facety! She thinks she's so hip in her clothes, but she always looks like she's wearing the clothes her grandmother gave her; which is probably the case.

Well, all that I can take. But then today Miss Halpern tells us she wants us to write a short story based on some aspect of our lives. Creative writing's got to be the thing I hate most. I get bored after writing one line! Anyway, she goes on and on about how she wants us to use '. . . *research as a means of getting information about your backgrounds* . . .' Which really means, bug your parents for the next seven days. I can't be bothered with all that. But Danucci and his crew think it's a great idea. Typical!

On our way home from school that afternoon, a crowd of us stopped by the newsagent's, ignoring the ten-foot-high sign that reads 'ONLY TWO KIDS AT A TIME'. And Danucci's in there with a couple of his trendy mates.

Hassle time!

Horace accidentally-on-purpose knocks into Danucci, whose nose is stuck in a music magazine. Danucci don't even glance up – Horace is well miffed. Then Takesha shoves me into Danucci and he almost drops the magazine. He glares at me. I'd never noticed his sparkling green eyes, his curly black eyelashes and . . .

'Nadine!'

My friends are all looking at me like I've grown a moustache or something. Danucci goes up to the counter with his mates to pay for the magazine. But not before giving me a look that could've had me ten foot under. For the first time I realize that he hates me as much as I hate him.

Talk about stress me out! I've got Miss Halpern on my back about that stupid short story I haven't written. Heather, Antoinette and Takesha on my back about fancying Danucci, and Horace on my back about going out with him. Well, before I crack up, I'm going to have one last go at getting some order into my life. *'Deal with each problem one at a time'* is my mum's favourite saying. First on my list is getting that story written.

Normally I never go near a library. Man, I break out in a cold sweat just thinking about one! But I force myself. The assignment's due in on Thursday and that's tomorrow! So in I go, on my own. I could've gone in with Antoinette and Takesha, as they love the library, but they'd already done their assignments. Heather *never* does assignments and she has the same aversion to libraries as I do – serious intellectual atmosphere, ughh!

I go straight upstairs to the study area. There are 'nuff kids in here, man! Swotting at the *beginning* of term? That's well sad, man! It's hunt for a seat time. I make my way past the tables. *No one was talking.* Can you believe that? Noses stuck in books. Disgusting! Ah-ha, a seat right by the window at the back. I could get away with eating my Mars bar without the crusty librarian seeing me. A freckle-faced, ginger-haired girl heads towards my seat. I throw myself into it. She gives me a filthy look and stomps off.

So I get out my exercise book and my Biros and take in the other kids around the table. Sangita, who's in the year below me; she lives in the library apparently. Tunde, a really quiet guy in my year – and the cleverest, Cheryl Watson, also in my year and a bookworm and . . . oh no! Danucci!

It's too late to move – there's nowhere else to sit. So I stay there silently cursing myself – 'til he looks up and sees me. (He'd had his head down in a computer book. That assignment's not due in 'til next month!) He kind of scowls at me, then returns to his book.

I can't concentrate on my story – it's that awkward. Ten minutes have gone by without us saying a word. This is driving me mad! I've got to say something!

'Look, I'm sorry about the other day in the newsagent's, but it weren't my fault.'

He looks at me, stunned, like he must've been preparing himself for aggro or something, particularly since none of his friends is around. But he still doesn't say anything.

'I said, I apologize. What d'you want, blood?' I hate being made to feel uncomfortable.

'Why?'

I can't work the boy out. 'Why what?'

'Why are you saying you're sorry when we both know you don't mean it?'

'Hey, you ain't in my head, so you don't know what's going on in there. But if you must know, I don't never say nothing that I don't mean. *"Better to offend than pretend"* is my motto.'

He folds his arms across his chest, looking triumphant. 'Not so hard without your mates, eh?'

'Neither are you.'

'I don't bother you, but you're *always* bothering me.'

A librarian near by tells us to be quiet, so we are for about half a minute. Then he goes: 'Is that your English assignment?'

I stop doodling on the page. 'Nah, I'm designing a hi-tech kitchen for my mum's birthday present.'

The librarian is glowering at us.

'So what's it going to be about?' Danucci asks.

'How the hell do I know?'

He's getting as narked as I am, and I feel my conscience prickling . . .

'I don't know what to write,' I whisper. 'I don't know *how* to write.'

'It's easy. Write about what you know.'

'Oh yeah? As easy as that? So what did you write about then.'

So Danucci tells me his short story. But he has to tell me outside 'cause we get kicked out.

Massimo, the guy in his story, is about eight or nine. He teases – no – bullies is more like it, his next-door neighbour's son Haresh, who's around two years younger. He'd call him 'paki' and stuff 'cause that's what all his friends at school did, bully Black and Asian kids. It was a mainly White school. Anyway, one day, Massimo's grandad Alfonso (I love the names) came to visit, overheard the name-calling and abuse and ordered Massimo inside. Alfonso told Massimo how hard it was for him being an Italian immigrant in the late thirties and forties because of Mussolini and that and also because he was well dark, being Sicilian. He told Massimo that he was shaming him by insulting Haresh. Massimo felt really bad because he loved his grandad (basically because he spoilt him rotten). Then Massimo ended up in a secondary school which was racially mixed and he had no problem forming friendships which rivalled the UN in their racial and cultural diversity.

'Our school's nothing like the UN.'

'So you guessed Massimo is based on me.'
'Just call me Einstein.'
He laughs.
'There's no way I could write like that.'
'Sure you can. Write about what you know.'
I look at him. 'I don't get it. Why are you helping me?'
He's about to answer when I spot my spars coming out of McDonald's. I freeze. Danucci sighs. 'You want me to disappear, right?'
They'll see us any time soon. So I goes, 'Well, you'd do the same.'
He's got that same look he had in the newsagent's. 'Would I?'
And he crosses the street in a huff just as they spot me.

The past three days have been a bummer, an all-time low. Oh, I got my assignment done and handed it in on time, no worries there. Except that it's crap. No, it's my friends that have been stressing me out – big time – with the Danucci thing. They've been saying that I'll be trading in Redrat for Jamiroquai. Yesterday, Horace got me so vexed that I cussed him about his nappy-never-see-comb head. As for Danucci, he won't so much as look at me. Worst of all, that's what's bugging me the most! I know now why I hated him so much. I was *making* myself hate him because I knew I *liked* him. But now with him ignoring me I feel so depressed I can't eat or sleep let alone think properly.

Enough is enough! I'm going to sort this mess out. So I write him a note and pull it in his desk before English class. If he still wants to know, he'll meet me by the huts after class.

'Ain't you afraid to be seen in public with me?'
I shrug my shoulders. I know he's pleased I left him that note. His green eyes are twinkling like crazy.
'I want to apologize.'
'Like last time?'
'You're making this really difficult.'
He leans against the wall. 'Good. You really pissed me off the other day.'
'I know and I've been suffering since.'
'Friends giving you a hard time?'
'*You're* giving me a hard time.'
Silence. I count the stripes on my hi-tops; one, two, three . . .

'I've always liked you Nadine.' He says it so softly.

'I'd never have guessed.'

'And as you wrote me a note . . .'

'Yeah, I like you, too. I guess I was trying to hide it by giving you a hard time.'

He smiles at me. 'I ain't saying it's going to be easy if we're friendly-like, my friends'll give me a hard time, too, you know. But I would never cross the street if they saw me with you. It depends on how much you want to be part of the crowd.'

'I've been really miserable since that day, I feel like I'd be living a lie if I kept . . . you know, pretending.'

'Better to offend than pretend, right?'

'Is Debra Haynes your girlfriend?'

He shakes his head. 'Is Horace Batchelor your boyfriend?'

I roll my eyes.

Then he pulls me close to him and we kiss. Then he puts his arm around me as we head towards the playground, where everyone will see us! I ain't going to lie and say I feel a hundred per cent comfortable about it. But for my own peace of mind, I've got to give it a go. Especially since I've just written a short story about it. I mean, it's got to be a first in our school: a ragga-loving junglis girl going with a trendy freaky deak.

SNOWDROP

By Mei Chi Chan

Outcomes

Discussion of Issues

Self doubt – making decisions
Breaking away – from family and tradition
Independence and freedom
Courage

TB 34

Literacy Work

Text level
Analysis of descriptive writing

TB 32

Word level
Symbolism

TB 33

Stimulus Page

As you read, take notice of the various techniques the writer uses to make the setting real to you. Look for information related to the five senses.

See if you can spot where the story changes from using the third person: 'She had come to tell them . . .' to using the first person: 'I . . .'

The title is simply *Snowdrop*. You'll find out why in the middle of the story. Using various research techniques, find out all you can about snowdrops before you begin to read.

One of the themes of this story is the relationship between parents and their children. Have you ever dreaded telling your parents or guardians something? What did you decide to do?

'She had come to tell them of her decision.' This is the first sentence of the story. What do you think she could be thinking about?

SNOWDROP

By Mei Chi Chan

She had come to tell them of her decision.

Standing by the door of the kitchen in the semi-darkness, a faint odour of bleach and onions greeted her like an old and comfortable companion. Silence, condensed by the hum of the refrigerators, echoed through and drew her in.

The florescent strips flickered before exploding off the hard, sharp surfaces, pricking out the edges, threatening the shadows. This was a kitchen that spoke not of home and its comforts but of forges, armoury and battle. For now, the steel rested. The oil in the deep fryer was cool, brown and thick as treacle. The heavy iron range stood dominating the room like an altar; the four holes cut side by side into its black metal looked curiously vulnerable to her, and she resisted the temptation to cover them up with the woks that huddled upside down like turtles beneath the range.

She walked across the room to the chopping board that stood on its own. Knives and choppers of different shapes and sizes hung from one of its edges, resembling a set of monstrous teeth. She could almost hear the thud of a heavy blade cleaving through flesh and bone onto the wood below. Delicately, she traced the scars on the surface. Tiny fragments of wood tickled her fingertips. In two hours her mother would come down the stairs and enter this arena. The fires would be lit, the oil would begin to bubble and steam and the steel would start to clash. She remembered Friday nights when she was a child. Friday was the busiest night of the week. People invaded the take-away in hordes after the pubs had closed. Reeking of cigarette smoke and with the sour smell of drink on their breath, they demanded to be fed. Inside the kitchen she would sit, unable to help: the still centre in the madly spinning wheel of movement around her. She would look backwards and forwards between her father and her mother. Their faces frightened her, she could not recognise them. They were not their daytime selves, they became something impersonal, mechanical, and even monstrous. They were like the knives, slashing, paring, chopping, slicing, dividing. Moving through the thick greasy white smoke like the warriors of old, advancing in the mists of dawn; they looked invincible. Every ounce of being was consumed in the task of making food. It could not be called 'cooking'. Cooking sounded too homely. No, like alchemists, they brought forth food out of steel and fire. Their creations subdued and sated the hungry hordes that bayed impatiently outside.

She walked over and bent down to pick up one of the steel woks beneath the range. She tested it for its weight, savouring the way it felt to grip the wooden handle in her hand and the tension stretching her wrist. She dropped it onto one of the holes and it made a dull clunk as it landed. She walked round and round the kitchen, circling the aluminum worktop that was the centrepiece of the room. At times, she would stride, eyes wide and blazing. Then at other times her steps turned into a shuffle. She sighed and muttered, shaking her head: *I can't, I can't do it, I can't, I really can't. They can. But not me. I'm too soft, too weak, too split. I don't have it – what it takes. I – will – fail.*

But there was another voice in her head, saying: *you can, you can do it. Of course you can. You have had the training. You have the guts. You have stamina. That's all you need. The rest will take care of itself.* She heard footsteps. She felt a shaking in the depths of her stomach. They would ask her and she would not know what to say . . .

'Snowdrop. That's a snowdrop.' The little girl listened deeply to the word. Gem-like, it sank into her heart and made it glow. A blue-green stem, a slender arch over virginal snow, and a white pendant flower dangling like an echo over it. 'A snowdrop.' That first, never-ending winter in England. Frosted air that bit her lungs, toes that never thawed, strangers made stranger still, wrapped and hunched and invisible in their layers, voices that blew like gusts into her ears, sound without meaning – until the word 'snowdrop'. Something melted. It was the feeling that she could not express then, the feeling of a fragile white flower rising over the snow. Now she would call it 'hope'. How thankful she was not to have known the word then.

They would ask her and she would say 'snowdrop' and they would understand. The word would turn like a key in their hearts. Snowdrop, snow-drop, a flower, a drop of . . .

Her mother and father broke into the space and light. She looked at them for a moment and there was confusion. In her mind they had been giants. Had they always been so small? How sallow and faded they looked, like parchment. In an instant, doubt vanished, and the two voices in her head united: *They cannot win. I will not be able to win here either. It is the wood, the metal, the blades, the oil, the flames – that last. It is the flesh and the spirit that are bowed and twisted for their purpose. Those warriors of myth and legend were invincible only in stories. Blood is spilt, flesh and bone are torn and shattered and burnt. Only the weapons remain unharmed: wood and metal gleaming as though smiling. The victory belongs to them. All the while we feared the hordes beyond; all the while they were among us here. And my parents, what is left of them?*

When she spoke, her voice was steady and clear. And when she told them that she would not stay and work in the kitchen they did not try to persuade her. Her father turned on the fryer and her mother lit the range.

ON THE SIDEWALK BLEEDING

By Evan Hunter

Outcomes

Discussion of Issues

What it means to be an individual
The power, and the dangers, of groups or gangs
Inner city violence and isolation

TB 37   TB 37

Literacy Work

Text Level
Structuring stories
Analysing the writer's ideas

TB 39   TB 36

Sentence Level
Effective sentences – repetition

TB 38

Drama and Oral Activities

Role play – before and after
Distilling meaning – oral presentation

TB 36

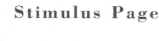

Stimulus Page

Before you begin reading, think about which is best: to be really independent, or to belong to a gang. What are the advantages and disadvantages?

Your school may have its own uniform. Can you think of other groups of people (who share beliefs or who like the same things) that also create their own unofficial 'uniform'? What does it often consist of?

One of the parables in The Bible tells the story of the 'Good Samaritan'. Some of you might know the story, or you could ask your teacher to read it to the class. As you read *On the Sidewalk Bleeding* see if you can find any similarities.

As you begin to read, see if you can pick up the clues which tell you where the story is set.

The writer chooses to begin with seven important words: 'The boy lay bleeding in the rain.' Why do you think he chose this beginning?

ON THE SIDEWALK BLEEDING

By Evan Hunter

The boy lay bleeding in the rain. He was sixteen years old, and he wore a bright purple silk jacket, and the lettering across the back of the jacket read THE ROYALS. The boy's name was Andy, and the name was written in black thread on the front of the jacket, just over the heart. *Andy.*

He had been stabbed ten minutes ago. The knife had entered just below his ribs, tearing a wide gap in his flesh. He lay on the sidewalk with the March rain drilling his jacket and drilling his body and washing away the blood that poured from his open wound. He had known terrible pain when the knife had torn across his body, then sudden relief when the blade was pulled away. He had heard the voice saying, 'That's for you, Royal!' and then the sound of footsteps hurrying into the rain, and then he had fallen to the sidewalk, clutching his stomach, trying to stop the flow of blood.

He tried to yell for help, but he had no voice. He did not know why his voice was gone, or why there was an open hole in his body from which his life ran redly. It was 11.30 p.m., but he did not know the time.

There was another thing he did not know.

He did not know he was dying. He lay on the sidewalk bleeding, and he thought only: *That was a fierce rumble. They got me good that time*, but he did not know he was dying. He would have been frightened had he known. He lay bleeding and wishing he could cry out for help, but there was no voice in his throat. There was only the bubbling of blood from between his lips whenever he opened his mouth to speak. He lay silent in his pain, waiting, waiting for someone to find him.

He could hear the sound of automobile tyres hushed on the rainswept streets, far away at the other end of the long alley. He could see the splash of neon at the other end of the alley. It was painting the pavement red and green.

He wondered if Laura would be angry.

He had left the jump to get a package of cigarettes. He had told her he would be back in a few minutes, and then he had gone downstairs and found the candy store closed. He knew that Alfredo's on the next block would be open. He had started through the alley, and that was when he'd been ambushed.

He could hear the faint sound of music now, coming from a long, long way off. He wondered if Laura was dancing, wondered if she had missed him yet. Maybe she thought he wasn't coming back. Maybe she thought he'd cut out for good. Maybe she'd already left the jump and gone home. He thought of her face, the brown eyes and the jet-black hair, and thinking of her he forgot his pain a little, forgot that blood was rushing from his body.

Someday he would marry Laura. Someday he would marry her, and they would have a lot of kids, and then they would get out of the neighbourhood. They would move to a clean project in the Bronx, or maybe they would move to Staten Island. When they were married, when they had kids.

He heard footsteps at the other end of the alley. He lifted his cheek from the sidewalk and looked into the darkness and tried to cry out, but again there was only a soft hissing bubble of blood on his mouth.

The man came down the alley. He had not seen Andy yet. He walked, and then stopped to lean against the brick of the building, and then walked again. He saw Andy then and came towards him, and he stood over him for a long time, the minutes ticking, ticking, watching him and not speaking.

Then he said, 'What's a matter, buddy?'

Andy could not speak, and he could barely move. He lifted his face slightly and looked up at the man. He smelled the sickening odour of alcohol. The man was drunk.

The man was smiling.

'Did you fall down, buddy?' he asked. 'You mus' be as drunk as I am.'

He squatted alongside Andy.

'You gonna catch cold here,' he said. 'What's a matter? You like layin' in the wet?'

Andy could not answer. The rain spattered around them.

'You like a drink?'

Andy shook his head.

'I gotta bottle. Here,' the man said. He pulled a pint bottle from his inside jacket pocket. Andy tried to move, but pain wrenched him back flat against the sidewalk.

'Take it,' the man said. He kept watching Andy. 'Take it.' When Andy did not move, he said, 'Nev' mind, I'll have one m'self.' He tilted the bottle to his lips, and then wiped the back of his hand across his mouth. 'You too young to be drinkin' anyway. Should be 'shamed of yourself, drunk an' laying in an alley, all wet. Shame on you. I gotta good minda calla cop.'

Andy nodded. Yes, he tried to say. Yes, call a cop. Please. Call one.

'Oh, you don't like that, huh?' the drunk said. 'You don' wanna cop to fin' you all drunk an' wet in an alley, huh? Okay, buddy. This time you get off easy.' He got to his feet. 'This time you lucky,' he said. He waved broadly at Andy, and then almost lost his footing. 'S'long, buddy,' he said.

Wait, Andy thought. *Wait please, I'm bleeding*.

'S'long,' the drunk said again. 'I see you aroun',' and then he staggered off up the alley.

Andy lay and thought: *Laura, Laura. Are you dancing?*

The couple came into the alley suddenly. They ran into the alley together, running from the rain. The boy held the girl's elbow, the girl spreading a newspaper over her head to protect her hair. Andy watched them run into the alley laughing, and then duck into the doorway not ten feet from him.

'Man, what rain!' the boy said. 'You could drown out there.'

'I have to get home,' the girl said. 'It's late, Freddie. I have to get home.'

'We got time,' Freddie said. 'Your people won't raise a fuss if you're a little late. Not with this kind of weather.'

'It's dark,' the girl said, and she giggled.

'Yeah,' the boy answered, his voice very low.

'Freddie . . .?'

'Um?'

'You're . . . you're standing very close to me.'

'Um.'

There was a long silence. Then the girl said, 'Oh,' only that single word, and Andy knew she'd been kissed. He suddenly hungered for Laura's mouth. It was then that he wondered if he would ever kiss Laura again. It was then that he wondered if he was dying.

No, he thought, *I can't be dying, not from a little street rumble, not from just getting cut. Guys get cut all the time in rumbles. I can't be dying. No, that's stupid. That don't make sense at all.*

'You shouldn't,' the girl said.

'Why not?'

'I don't know.'

'Do you like it?'

'Yes.'

'So?'

'I don't know.'

'I love you, Angela,' the boy said.

'I love you, too, Freddie,' the girl said, and Andy listened and thought: *I love you, Laura. Laura, I think maybe I'm dying. Laura, this is stupid but I think I'm dying. Laura, I think I'm dying!*

He tried to speak. He tried to move. He tried to crawl towards the doorway. He tried to make a noise, a sound, and a grunt came from his lips. He tried again, and another grunt came, a low animal grunt of pain.

'What was that?' the girl said, breaking away from the boy.

'I don't know,' he answered.

'Go look, Freddie.'

'No. Wait.'

Andy moved his lips again. Again the sound came from him.

'Freddie!'

'What?'

'I'm scared.'

'I'll go see,' the boy said.

He stepped into the alley. He walked over to where Andy lay on the ground. He stood over him, watching him.

'You all right?' he asked.

'What is it?' Angela said from the doorway.

'Somebody's hurt,' Freddie said.

'Let's get out of here,' Angela said.

'No. Wait a minute.' He knelt down beside Andy. 'You cut?' he asked.

Andy nodded. The boy kept looking at him. He saw the lettering on the jacket then. THE ROYALS. He turned to Angela.

'He's a Royal,' he said.

'Let's . . . what . . . what do you want to do, Freddie?'

'I don't know. I don't want to get mixed up in this. He's a Royal. We help him, and the Guardians'll be down on our necks. I don't want to get mixed up in this, Angela.'

'Is he . . . is he hurt bad?'

'Yeah, it looks that way.'

'What shall we do?'

'I don't know.'

'We can't leave him here in the rain.' Angela hesitated. 'Can we?'

'If we get a cop, the Guardians'll find out who,' Freddie said. 'I don't know, Angela, I don't know.'

Angela hesitated a long time before answering. Then she said, 'I have to go home, Freddie. My people will begin to worry.'

'Yeah,' Freddie said. He looked at Andy again. 'You all right?' he asked. Andy lifted his face from the sidewalk, and his eyes said: *Please, please help me*, and maybe Freddie read what his eyes were saying, and maybe he didn't.

Behind him, Angela said, 'Freddie, let's get out of here! Please!' Freddie stood up. He looked at Andy again, and then mumbled, 'I'm sorry.' He took Angela's arm, and together they ran towards the neon splash at the other end of the alley.

Why, they're afraid of the Guardians, Andy thought in amazement. *But why shouldn't they be? I wasn't afraid of the Guardians. I never turkeyed out of a rumble with the Guardians. I got heart. But I'm bleeding.*

The rain was soothing. It was a cold rain, but his body was hot all over, and the rain helped cool him. He had always liked rain. He could remember sitting in Laura's house one time, the rain running down the windows, and just looking out over the street, watching the people running from the rain. That was when he'd first joined the Royals. He could remember how happy he was the Royals had taken him. The Royals and the Guardians, two of the biggest. He was a Royal. There had been meaning to the title.

Now, in the alley, with the cold rain washing his hot body, he wondered about the meaning. If he died, he was Andy. He was not a Royal. He was simply Andy, and he was dead. And he wondered suddenly if the Guardians who had ambushed him and knifed him had ever once realised he was Andy? Had they known that he was Andy, or had they simply known that he was a Royal wearing a purple silk jacket? Had they stabbed *him*, Andy, or had they only stabbed the jacket and the title, and what good was the title if you were dying?

I'm Andy, he screamed wordlessly. *I'm Andy.*

An old lady stopped at the other end of the alley. The garbage cans were stacked there, beating noisily in the rain. The old lady carried an umbrella with broken ribs, carried it like a queen. She stepped into the mouth of the alley, shopping bag over one arm. She lifted the lids of the garbage cans. She did not hear Andy grunt because she was a little deaf and because the rain was beating on the cans. She collected her string and her newspapers, and an old hat with a feather on it from one of the garbage cans, and a broken footstool from another of the cans. And then she replaced the lids and lifted her umbrella high and walked out of the alley mouth. She had worked quickly and soundlessly, and now she was gone.

The alley looked very long now. He could see people passing at the other end of it, and he wondered who the people were, and he wondered if he would ever get to know them, wondered who it was on the Guardians who had stabbed him, who had plunged the knife into his body.

'That's for you, Royal!' the voice had said. 'That's for you, Royal!' Even in his pain, there had been some sort of pride in knowing he was a Royal. Now there was no pride at all. With the rain beginning to chill him, with the blood pouring steadily between his fingers, he knew only a sort of dizziness. He could only think: *I want to be Andy.*

It was not very much to ask of the world.

He watched the world passing at the other end of the alley. The world didn't know he was Andy. The world didn't know he was alive. He wanted to say, 'Hey, I'm alive! Hey, look at me! I'm alive! Don't you know I'm alive! Don't you know I exist?'

He felt weak and very tired. He felt alone and wet and feverish and chilled. He knew he was going to die now. That made him suddenly sad. He was filled with sadness that his life would be over at sixteen. He felt at once as if he had never done anything, never been anywhere. There were so many things to do. He wondered why he'd never thought of them before, wondered why the rumbles and the jumps and the purple jackets had always seemed so important to him before. Now they seemed like such small things in a world he was missing, a world that was rushing past at the other end of the alley.

I don't want to die, he thought. *I haven't lived yet.*

It seemed very important to him that he take off the purple jacket. He was very close to dying, and when they found him, he did not want them to say, 'Oh, it's a Royal.' With great effort, he rolled over on to his back. He felt the pain tearing at his stomach when he moved. If he never did another thing, he wanted to take off the jacket. The jacket had only one meaning now, and that was a very simple meaning.

If he had not been wearing the jacket, he wouldn't have been stabbed. The knife had not been plunged in hatred of Andy. The knife hated only the purple jacket. The jacket was a stupid meaningless thing that was robbing him of his life.

He lay struggling with the shiny wet jacket. His arms were heavy. Pain ripped fire across his body whenever he moved. But he squirmed and fought and twisted until one arm was free and then the other. He rolled away from the jacket and lay quite still, breathing heavily, listening to the sound of his breathing and the sounds of the rain and thinking: *Rain is sweet, I'm Andy.*

She found him in the doorway a minute past midnight. She left the dance to look for him. When she found him she knelt beside him and said, 'Andy, it's me, Laura.'

He did not answer her. She backed away from him, tears springing into her eyes, and then she ran from the alley. She did not stop running until she found a cop.

And now, standing with the cop, she looked down at him. The cop rose and said, 'He's dead.' All the crying was out of her now. She stood in the rain and said nothing, looking at the dead boy on the pavement, and looking at the purple jacket that rested a foot away from his body.

The cop picked up the jacket and turned it over in his hands.

'A Royal, huh?' he said.

She looked at the cop, and, very quietly, she said, 'His name is Andy.'

The cop slung the jacket over his arm. He took out his black pad, and he flipped it open to a blank page.

'A Royal,' he said.

Then he began writing.

THE ONES WHO WALK AWAY FROM OMELAS*

By Ursula Le Guin

Outcomes

Discussion of Issues

Contrasts within society
Charity
The requirements for happiness

Literacy Work

Text Level
Storytelling techniques – addressing the reader
Searching for meanings

Sentence Level
Use of first and third person
Use of colour in descriptive sentences

Word Level
Advanced vocabulary
Political and sociological language

Drama and Oral Activities

Hot-seating characters
Debating the issues raised

*Please note these stories contain strong language.

Stimulus Page

In this story, the writer builds an imaginary city with words. Can you think of other stories that do this? See how many films you can name which do the same thing using images.

As you read, notice how the writer describes the city and its people. There are no named characters. She is describing a society, with all its customs, traditions and secrets.

You also need to look for the places where the writer speaks to the reader directly. She does this several times. Where does it start?

You might like to compare this story with *Two Islands* by Ivan Gantschev (page 81), as there are several similarities. There are also links with Creation stories from different cultures.

This is a very challenging and shocking story. It has many beautiful things in it, but it also has some disturbing things. There are no easy answers to the puzzles within the story, so be prepared to have an open mind, and enjoy trying to solve them all!

THE ONES WHO WALK AWAY FROM OMELAS

By Ursula Le Guin

With a clamour of bells that set the swallows soaring, the Festival of Summer came to the city of Omelas, bright-towered by the sea. The rigging of the boats in harbor sparkled with flags. In the streets between houses with red roofs and painted walls, between old moss-grown gardens and under avenues of trees, past great parks and public buildings, processions moved. Some were decorous: old people in long stiff robes of mauve and grey, grave master workmen, quiet, merry women carrying their babies and chatting as they walked. In other streets the music beat faster, a shimmering of gong and tambourine, and the people went dancing, the procession was a dance. Children dodged in and out, their high calls rising like the swallows' crossing flights over the music and the singing. All the processions wound towards the north side of the city, where on the great water-meadow called the Green Fields boys and girls, naked in the bright air, with mud-stained feet and ankles and long, lithe arms, exercised their restive horses before the race.

The horses wore no gear at all but a halter without bit. Their manes were braided with streamers of silver, gold and green. They flared their nostrils and pranced and boasted to one another; they were vastly excited, the horse being the only animal who has adopted our ceremonies as his own. Far off to the north and west the mountains stood up half encircling Omelas on her bay. The air of morning was so clear that the snow still crowning the Eighteen Peaks burned with white-gold fire across the miles of sunlit air, under the dark blue of the sky.

There was just enough wind to make the banners that marked the racecourse snap and flutter now and then. In the silence of the broad green meadows one could hear the music winding through the city streets, farther and nearer and ever approaching, a cheerful faint sweetness of the air that from time to time trembled and gathered together and broke out into the great joyous clanging of the bells. Joyous! How is one to tell about joy? How describe the citizens of Omelas? They were not simple folk, you see, though they were happy. But we do not say the words of cheer much any more. All smiles have become archaic. Given a description such as this one tends to make certain assumptions. Given a description such as this one tends to look next for the King, mounted on a splendid stallion and surrounded by his noble knights, or perhaps in a golden-litter borne by great-muscled slaves. But there was no king. They did not use swords, or keep slaves. They were not barbarians. I do not know the rules and laws of their society, but I suspect that they were singularly few. As they did without monarchy and slavery, so they also got on without the stock exchange, the advertisement, the secret police, and the bomb. Yet I repeat that these were not simple folk, not dulcet shepherds, noble savages, bland utopians. They were not less complex than us.

The trouble is that we have a bad habit, encouraged by pedants and sophisticates, of considering happiness as something rather stupid. Only pain is intellectual, only evil interesting. This is the treason of the artist; a refusal to admit the banality of evil and the terrible boredom of pain. If you can't lick 'em, join 'em. If it hurts, repeat it. But to praise despair is to condemn delight, to embrace violence is to lose hold of everything else. We have almost lost hold; we can no longer describe a happy man, nor make any celebrations of joy. How can I tell you about the people of Omelas?

They were not naive and happy children – though their children were, in fact, happy. They were mature, intelligent, passionate adults whose lives were not wretched. O miracle! but I wish I could describe it better. I wish I could convince you. Omelas sounds in my words like a city in a fairy tale, long ago and far away, once upon a time. Perhaps it would be best if you imagined it as your own fancy bids, assuming it will rise to the occasion, for certainly I cannot suit you all. For instance, how about technology? I think that there would be no cars or helicopters in and above the streets; this follows from the fact that the people of Omelas are happy people. Happiness is based on a just discrimination of what is necessary, what is neither necessary nor destructive, and what is destructive. In the middle category, however – that of the unnecessary but undestructive, that of comfort, luxury, exuberance, etc., etc. – they could perfectly well have central heating, subway trains, washing machines, and all kinds of marvellous devices not yet invented here, floating light-sources, fuelless power, a cure for the common cold. Or they could have none of that; it doesn't matter. As you like it. I incline to think that people from towns up and down the coast have been coming in to Omelas during the last days before the Festival on very fast little trains and double-decked trams, and that the train station of Omelas is actually the handsomest building in town, though plainer than the magnificent Farmers' Market.

But even granted trains, I fear that Omelas so far strikes some of you as goody-goody. Smiles, bells, parades, horses, bleh. If so, please add an orgy. If an orgy would help, don't hesitate. Let us not, however, have temples from which issue beautiful nude priests and priestesses already half in ecstasy and ready to copulate with any man or woman, lover or stranger, who desires union with the deep godhead of the blood, although that was my first idea. But really it would be better not to have any temples in Omelas – at least, not manned temples. Religion yes, clergy no. Surely the beautiful nudes can just wander about offering themselves like divine souffles to the hunger of the needy and the rapture of the flesh. Let them join the processions. Let tambourines be struck above the copulations, and the glory of desire be proclaimed upon the gongs and (a not unimportant point) let the offspring of these delightful rituals be beloved and looked after by all. One thing I know there is none of in Omelas is guilt. But what else should there be? I thought at first there were no drugs, but that is puritanical. For those who like it, the faint insistent sweetness of DROOZ may perfume the ways of the City, DROOZ which first brings a great lightness and brilliance to the mind and limbs, and then after some hours a dreamy languor, and wonderful visions at last of the very arcana and inmost secrets of the Universe, as well as exciting the pleasure of sex beyond all belief; and it is not habit-forming. For more modest tastes I think there ought to be beer. What else, what else belongs in the joyous city? The sense of victory, surely, the celebration of courage. But as we did without clergy, let us do without soldiers. The joy built upon successful slaughter is not the right kind of joy; it will not do, it is fearful and it is trivial. A boundless and generous contentment, a magnanimous triumph felt not against some outer enemy but in communion with the finest and fairest in the souls of all men everywhere and the splendour of the world's summer: this is what swells the hearts of the people of Omelas, and the victory they celebrate is that of life. I really don't think many of them need to take DROOZ.

Most of the processions have reached the Green Fields by now. A marvellous smell of cooking goes forth from the red and blue tents of the provisioners. The faces of small children are amiably sticky; in the benign grey beard of a man a couple of crumbs of rich pastry are entangled. The youths and girls have mounted their horses and are beginning to group around the starting line of the course. An old woman, small, fat and laughing, is passing out flowers from a basket, and tall young men wear her flowers in their shining hair. A child of nine or ten sits at the edge of the crowd, alone, playing on a wooden flute. People pause to listen, and they smile, but they do not speak to him for he never ceases playing and never sees them, his dark eyes wholly rapt in the sweet, thin magic of the tune.

He finishes, and slowly lowers his hands holding the wooden flute.

As if that little private silence were the signal, all at once a trumpet sounds from the pavilion near the starting line: imperious, melancholy, piercing. The horses rear on their slender legs, and some of them neigh in answer. Sober-faced, the young riders stroke the horses' necks and soothe them, whispering 'Quiet, quiet, there my beauty, my hope . . .'. They begin to form in rank along the starting line. The crowds along the racecourse are like a field of grass and flowers in the wind. The Festival of Summer has begun.

Do you believe? Do you accept the Festival, the city the joy? No? Then let me describe one more thing.

In a basement under one of the beautiful public buildings of Omelas, or perhaps in the cellar of one of its spacious private homes, there is a room. It has one locked door, and no window. A little light seeps in dustily between cracks in the boards, secondhand from a cobwebbed window somewhere across the cellar. In one corner of the little room a couple of mops, with stiff, clotted, foul-smelling heads, stand near a rusty bucket. The floor is dirt, a little damp to the touch, as cellar dirt usually is. The room is about three paces long and two wide: a mere broom closet or disused tool room. In the room a child is sitting. It could be a boy or a girl. It looks about six, but actually is nearly ten. It is feeble-minded. Perhaps it was born defective, or perhaps it has become imbecile through fear, malnutrition and neglect. It picks its nose and occasionally fumbles vaguely with its toes or genitals, as it sits hunched in the corner farthest from the bucket and two mops. It is afraid of the mops. It finds them horrible. It shuts its eyes, but it knows the mops are still standing there; and the door is locked; and nobody will come. The door is always locked; and nobody ever comes, except that sometimes – the child has no understanding of time or interval – sometimes the door rattles terribly and opens, and a person, or several people, are there. One of them may come in and kick the child to make it stand up. The others never come close, but peer in at it with frightened disgusted eyes. The food bowl and the water jug are hastily filled, the door is locked, the eyes disappear. The people at the door never say anything, but the child, who has not always lived in the tool room and can remember sunlight and its mother's voice, sometimes speaks 'I will be good' it says. 'Please let me out, I will be good!' They never answer. The child used to scream for help at night, and cry a good deal, but now it only makes a kind of whining, 'eh-haa, eh-haa', and it speaks less and less often. It is so thin there are no calves to its legs; its belly protrudes; it lives on a half-bowl of corn meal and grease a day. It is naked. Its buttocks and thighs are a mass of festered sores, as it sits in its own excrement continually.

They all know it is there, all the people of Omelas. Some of them have come to see it, others are content merely to know it is there. They all know that it has to be there. Some of them understand why, and some do not, but they all understand that their happiness, the beauty of the city, the tenderness of their friendships, the health of their children, the wisdom of their scholars, the skill of their makers, even the abundance of their harvest and the kindly weathers of their skies, depend wholly on this child's abominable misery.

This is usually explained to children when they are between eight and twelve, whenever they seem capable of understanding, and most of those who come to see the child are young people, though often enough an adult comes, or comes back to see the child. No matter how well the matter has been explained to them, these young spectators are always shocked and sickened at the sight. They feel disgust, which they had thought themselves superior to. They feel anger, outrage, impotence, despite all the explanations. They would like to do something for the child. But there is nothing they can do. If the child were brought up into the sunlight out of that vile place, if it were cleaned and fed and comforted, that would be a good thing, indeed; but if it were done, in that day and hour all the prosperity and beauty and delight of Omelas would wither and be destroyed. Those are the terms. To exchange all the goodness and grace of every life in Omelas for that single, small improvement: to throw away all the happiness of thousands for the chance of the happiness of one: that would let guilt within the walls indeed.

The terms are strict and absolute; there may not even be a kind word spoken to the child.

Often the young people go home in tears, or in a tearless rage, when they have seen the child and faced this terrible paradox. They may brood over it for weeks or years. But as time goes on they begin to realise that even if the child could be released, it would not get much good of its freedom: a little vague pleasure of warmth and food, no doubt, but little more. It is too degraded and imbecile to know any real joy. It has been afraid too long ever to be free. Its habits are too uncouth for it to respond to humane treatment. Indeed after so long it would probably be wretched without walls about it to protect it, and darkness for its eyes, and its own excrement to sit in. Their tears at the bitter injustice dry when they begin to perceive the terrible justice of reality and to accept it. Yet it is their tears and anger, the trying of their generosity and the acceptance of their helplessness, which are perhaps the true source of the splendour of their lives. Theirs is no vapid, irresponsible happiness. They know that they, like the child, are not free. They know compassion. It is the existence of the child, and their knowledge of its existence, that makes possible the nobility of their architecture, the poignancy of their music, the profundity of their science. It is because of the child that they are so gentle with children. They know that if the wretched one were not there snivelling in the dark, the other one, the flute-player could make no joyful music as the young riders line up in their beauty for the race in the sunlight of the first morning of summer.

Now do you believe in them? Are they not more credible? But there is one more thing to tell, and this is quite incredible.

At times one of the adolescent girls or boys who go to see the child does not go home to weep or rage, does not, in fact go home at all. Sometimes also a man or woman much older falls silent for a day or two, and then leaves home. These people go out into the street, and walk straight out of the city of Omelas, through the beautiful gates. They keep walking across the farmlands of Omelas. Each one goes alone, youth or girl, man or woman. Night falls; the traveller must pass down the village streets, between the houses with yellow-lit windows, and on out into the darkness of the fields. Each alone, they go west or north, towards the mountains. They go on. They leave Omelas, they walk ahead into the darkness and they do not come back. The place they go towards is a place even less imaginable to most of us than the city of happiness. I cannot describe it at all. It is possible that it does not exist. But they seem to know where they are going, the ones who walk away from Omelas.

(Variations on a theme by William James.)

TWO ISLANDS

By Ivan Gantschev

Outcomes

Discussion of Issues

Industrial development vs. concern of the environment
Materialism vs. spiritualism
Collaboration vs. dominance

Literacy Work

Text Level
Allegorical writing – what are the basic elements of an allegory?
TB 45

Sentence Level
Epitaphs – what they are and how to write them
TB 44

Word Level
Contrasting lexicons – an industrial word bag and a natural word bag
TB 44

Drama and Oral Activities

Pupils will have opportunities for paired improvisation and forum theatre work, as well as a number of extension activities
TB 45

Citizenship

Pupils will be asked to consider what a 'manifesto' is, and how the values and aspirations it contains might relate to their lives
TB 44

With thanks to Jonothan Neelands for his drama work on this story.

Stimulus Page

Imagine, if you can, two uninhabited islands in the middle of a blue ocean. Discuss with your partner what those islands might be like. Make a short list of features and discuss it with your group.

Find out about 'The Garden of Eden' and what it was like. You could use the Internet, your school's library or a copy of The Bible.

Try to find examples of tribes that live in remote areas away from any 'modern' influences, like television or hospitals. Perhaps your Geography teacher could help?

Discuss with your partner: do people have the right to live by their own rules without interference from other groups of people? Why?

If you lived on an island and you were in charge, what rules would you make for people to live by?

TWO ISLANDS

By Ivan Gantschev

Once there were two islands, Greenel and Graynel. They sat in the middle of the ocean with a wide stretch of deep water between them. The very first people who came to the island of Greenel found a peaceful place with tall green trees and dark, fertile soil. Their leaders said, 'Since we are here in the middle of the ocean, and our island is only so big and no bigger, we will all have to work very hard to tend it and keep it as lovely as it is today. If we are careful and wise we will be able to grow our own food and learn to make the other things we need to be happy and comfortable.'

And down through the years, that is the way it was on Greenel. Life was simple and it moved at the pace of the sun and the moon and the changing seasons.

The first people who ever came to Graynel found an island very similar to Greenel – quiet and green and lovely. But their leaders said: 'Since our new land is here in the middle of the ocean and is only so big and no bigger, we will have to work very hard if we are to keep up with the rest of the world. We will have to build ships and factories and use all of our land very wisely or we will never be able to make and buy all the things we want.'

There were changes on Graynel, big changes. Even though the island was small, it kept up with the world, and life on Graynel moved at the pace of the shipping timetables, the factory clocks and the traffic lights.

Life on Graynel became very complicated. There were so many factories to run, so many clocks to keep set on the same time, and so many highways to build, that the people of Graynel decided they needed someone who could take charge of the whole island.

And so they elected Gordon D. Warden to be The Boss. He promised that if he were The Boss then Graynel would be the best and the richest and the busiest and the most famous little island in all the world. He also promised that there would be jobs and cars and money and plenty of everything for everyone.

What he said was true. In a very short time there were so many more factories built that almost everyone had two jobs. The people had so much money to spend that everyone had at least one car, and they had so much money left over to save that there were more banks than there were gas stations. The citizens of Graynel were so pleased with all this progress that statues honouring Gordon D. Warden popped up all over the island.

Because all the land was needed for building and factories and highways, the whole island seemed like one big city. Where there used to be fields and forests, there were only a few tiny parks, just big enough for one or two people to visit at a time.

The very old people could remember when Graynel had been like a lovely garden in the sea; but the children of Graynel grew up thinking that it was normal to wear gas masks, and the only time they ever saw blue skies and green fields was when they tuned in to the Vacation Channel on TV.

When the great cargo ships and airplanes went past Greenel on their way to and from the busy ports of Graynel, the crews and the passengers always looked longingly at the clean air, the green hills, and the tidy little farms and towns. Businessmen came to Greenel to try to sell some of the things made in Graynel. But they always left disappointed because the people of Greenel had everything they needed.

Finally, when even the tiny parks had been squeezed out by the roads and the factories and the skyscrapers, the people of Graynel went to Gordon D. Warden and said, 'We need green fields and clean beaches and blue skies, just like they have on Greenel.'

This was a problem for Gordon D. Warden. He was not about to tear down any factories or rip up any highways – that would cost too much money. So he came up with a plan. Because his plan involved Greenel, he went there to present it himself.

When he met with the president of Greenel, Gordon D. Warden uncovered a big model he had brought with him. He said, 'This bridge is the greatest idea I've ever had. Your people will be able to go shopping on Graynel any time they choose, and my people will be able to drive over to Greenel whenever they need a little vacation. It will be the world's longest bridge, so tourists will come here from everywhere just to drive their cars across it. And it won't cost you one penny. What do you say? Is it a deal?'

The President of Greenel thought for a minute or two, and then said, 'I'm sorry, but if you built this bridge, our people would soon be building highways and gas stations and refineries and repair shops and hotels and restaurants – maybe even factories. Before long, our island would be just like Graynel. You and your people are always welcome to visit, or even to come and live as we do. But we want to keep Greenel just like it is.'

Gordon D. Warden was furious! Imagine this country boy wanting to be left out of the best idea of the century! He stood up from the table without saying a word, stomped back to his helicopter, and flew home to Graynel. And he said to himself, 'We're going to build that bridge anyway, and if they don't like it, just let them try to stop us!'

The next day, when Gordon D. Warden announced his plans to the citizens of Graynel, some of the people felt it was wrong to build a bridge if the people of Greenel did not want it. But most of them decided that if they could have the clean beaches and the green hills of Greenel as a vacation spot, well, so what if those bumpkins griped about it? And the factory owners and the bankers were thrilled, because it would take a lot of money and a lot of steel and concrete to build the world's longest bridge.

The people who did not think it was right to build the bridge protested and carried signs and wrote letters to the newspapers. They got to be such a problem for Gordon D. Warden that he declared them all traitors and gave them ten days to leave the island. Many of those who left went to live on Greenel.

All the ships from Graynel travelled to far-off lands, and every day they brought back load after load of wire and steel and rock and cement. Just to be sure that he got his way, Gordon D. Warden had some of the factories start building army tanks and big cannons. He told his citizens, 'If those people won't listen to reason, let them listen to the sound of our guns!'

When the last fifty shiploads of steel and rocks and cement were unloaded on the shores of Warden Bay, there was a huge rally to celebrate the first day of construction. The Boss had announced that he would come and throw the first stone into the sea to signal the start of the work. Gordon D. Warden arrived in a clattery cloud of dust and exhaust. The people all began to jump up and down, yelling, 'Speech! Speech! Speech!' He raised his arms to signal for silence, and a great hush settled over the crowd.

Just as Gordon D. Warden started to speak, there was a deep, shaking rumbling sound, as if a huge thunderstorm were caught inside a cave.

Crashes and screams, splashes and cracks and crumbling! Hissing steam and popping bubbles . . . and then silence.

In less than a minute, the whole island of Graynel had tipped up on its edge and slid down into the oily brown water of Warden Bay. Gordon D. Warden, the heavy building materials, the weapons, and all the people and cars and factories and everything else went straight to the bottom of the sea.

With the help of an old, old map, Graynel can still be found. There is no noise now, no smoke, no busy port with fleets of ships. All that remains is one lone chimney, sticking up out of the sea. The people of Greenel have fastened a sign to it, and anyone who travels past in a boat can read what the sign says.

THE ASSIGNMENT

By Saadat Hasan Manto

Outcomes

Discussion of Issues

Inter-racial violence
Trust and betrayal
Citizenship: bullying

Literacy Work

Text Level
Diary writing

Sentence Level
Openings and endings
Analysing language

TB 49

TB 48   **TB 47**

Stimulus Page

Why does violence begin between different groups of people? Look through a collection of newspapers and find examples of conflict across the globe. Report back to your group on what you find.

This story is set in the Indian city of Amritsar. Use an atlas to find out where it is.

The narrative involves violence between extremists who don't care what happens to ordinary, decent Muslims and Hindus. Go to the library, look in reference books or use the Internet to find out about these two religious groups.

In Indian culture, children are very respectful towards their parents; especially towards fathers, and they would never dream of disobeying or answering back. Is this always a good thing? What is it like in your culture? Discuss in pairs and feedback to the rest of your group.

Have you ever been frightened by events in your community? Discuss your experiences with a friend. Then, read on . . .

THE ASSIGNMENT

By Saadat Hasan Manto
(Translated from the Urdu)

Beginning with isolated incidents of stabbing, it had now developed into full-scale communal violence, with no holds barred. Even home-made bombs were being used.

The general view in Amritsar was that the riots could not last long. They were seen as no more than a manifestation of temporarily inflamed political passions which were bound to cool down before long. After all, these were not the first communal riots the city had known. There had been so many of them in the past. They never lasted long. The pattern was familiar. Two weeks or so of unrest and then business as usual. On the basis of experience, therefore, the people were quite justified in believing that the current troubles would also run their course in a few days. But this did not happen. They not only continued, but grew in intensity.

Muslims living in Hindu localities began to leave for safer places, and Hindus in Muslim majority areas followed suit. However, everyone saw these adjustments as strictly temporary. The atmosphere would soon be clear of this communal madness, they told themselves.

Retired judge Mian Adbul Hai was absolutely confident that things would return to normal soon, which was why he wasn't worried. He had two children, a boy of eleven and a girl of seventeen. In addition, there was an old servant who was now pushing seventy. It was a small family. When the troubles started,

Mian *sahib*[1], being an extra cautious man, stocked up on food . . . just in case. So on one count, at least, there were no worries.

His daughter Sughra was less sure of things. They lived in a three-storey house with a view over almost the entire city. Sughra could not help noticing that whenever she went on the roof, there were fires raging everywhere. In the beginning, she could hear fire engines rushing past, their bells ringing, but this had now stopped. There were too many fires in too many places.

The nights had become particularly frightening. The sky was always lit by conflagrations like giants spitting out flames. Then there were the slogans which rent the air with terrifying frequency – Allaho Akbar, Har Har Mahadev.

Sughra never expressed her fears to her father, because he had declared confidently that there was no cause for anxiety. Everything was going to be fine. Since he was generally always right, she had initially felt reassured.

However, when the power and water supplies were suddenly cut off, she expressed her unease to her father and suggested apologetically that, for a few days at least, they should move to Sharifpura, a Muslim locality, to where many of the old residents had already moved. Mian sahib was adamant: 'You're imagining things. Everything is going to be normal very soon.'

He was wrong. Things went from bad to worse. Before long there was not a single Muslim family to be found in Mian Abdul Hai's locality. Then one day Mian sahib suffered a stroke and was laid up. His son Basharat, who used to spend most of his time playing self-devised games, now stayed glued to his father's bed.

All the shops in the area had been permanently boarded up. Dr Ghulam Hussain's dispensary had been shut for weeks and Sughra had noticed from the roof-top one day that the adjoining clinic of Dr Goranditta Mall was also closed. Mian sahib's condition was getting worse day by day. Sughra was almost at the end of her wits. One day she took Basharat aside and said to him, 'You've got to do something. I know it's not safe to go out, but we must get some help. Our father is very ill.'

The boy went, but came back almost immediately. His face was pale with fear. He had seen a blood-drenched body lying in the street and a group of wild-looking men looting shops. Sughra took the terrified boy in her arms and said a silent prayer, thanking

[1] sir, master

God for his safe return. However, she could not bear her father's suffering. His left side was now completely lifeless. His speech had been impaired and he mostly communicated through gestures, all designed to reassure Sughra that soon all would be well.

It was the month of Ramadan and only two days to Id[2]. Mian sahib was quite confident that the troubles would be over by then. He was again wrong. A canopy of smoke hung over the city, with fires burning everywhere. At night the silence was shattered by deafening explosions. Sughra and Basharat hadn't slept for days.

Sughra, in any case, couldn't because of her father's deteriorating condition. Helplessly, she would look at him, then at her young frightened brother and the seventy-year-old servant Akbar, who was useless for all practical purposes. He mostly kept to his bed, coughing and fighting for breath. One day Sughra told him angrily, 'What good are you? Do you realise how ill Mian sahib is? Perhaps you are too lazy to want to help, pretending that you are suffering from acute asthma. There was a time when servants used to sacrifice their lives for their masters.'

Sughra felt very bad afterwards. She had been unnecessarily harsh on the old man. In the evening when she took his food to him in his small room, he was not there. Basharat looked for him all over the house but he was nowhere to be found. The front door was unlatched. He was gone, perhaps to get some help for Mian sahib. Sughra prayed for his return, but two days passed and he hadn't come back.

It was evening and the festival of Id was now only a day away. She remembered the excitement which used to grip the family on this occasion. She remembered standing on the roof-top, peering into the sky, looking for the Id moon and praying for the clouds to clear. But how different everything was today. The sky was covered in smoke and on distant roofs one could see people looking upwards. Were they trying to catch sight of the new moon or were they watching the fires, she wondered?

She looked up and saw the thin sliver of the moon peeping through a small patch in the sky. She raised her hands in prayer, begging God to make her father well. Basharat, however, was upset that there would be no Id this year.

The night hadn't yet fallen. Sughra had moved her father's bed out of the room onto the veranda. She was sprinkling water on the

[2] a Muslim festival

floor to make it cool. Mian sahib was lying there quietly looking with vacant eyes at the sky where she had seen the moon. Sughra came and sat next to him. He motioned her to get closer. Then he raised his right arm slowly and put it on her head. Tears began to run from Sughra's eyes. Even Mian sahib looked moved. Then with great difficulty he said to her, 'God is merciful. All will be well.'

Suddenly there was a knock on the door. Sughra's heart began to beat violently. She looked at Basharat, whose face had turned white like a sheet of paper. There was another knock. Mian sahib gestured to Sughra to answer it. It must be old Akbar who had come back, she thought. She said to Basharat, 'Answer the door. I'm sure it's Akbar.' Her father shook his head, as if to signal disagreement.

'Then who can it be?' Sughra asked him.

Mian Abdul Hai tried to speak, but before he could do so, Basharat came running in. He was breathless. Taking Sughra aside, he whispered, 'It's a Sikh.'

Sughra screamed, 'A Sikh! What does he want?'

'He wants me to open the door.'

Sughra took Basharat in her arms and went and sat on her father's bed, looking at him desolately.

On Mian Abdul Hai's thin, lifeless lips, a faint smile appeared. 'Go and open the door. It is Gurmukh Singh.'

'No, it's someone else,' Basharat said.

Mian sahib turned to Sughra. 'Open the door. It's him.'

Sughra rose. She knew Gurmukh Singh. Her father had once done him a favour. He had been involved in a false legal suit and Mian sahib had acquitted him. That was a long time ago, but every year on the occasion of Id, he would come all the way from his village with a bag of home-made noodles. Mian sahib had told him several times, 'Sardar sahib, you really are too kind. You shouldn't inconvenience yourself every year.' But Gurmukh Singh would always reply, 'Mian sahib, God has given you everything. This is only a small gift which I bring every year in humble acknowledgement of the kindness you did me once. Even a hundred generations of mine would not be able to repay your favour. May God keep you happy.'

Sughra was reassured. Why hadn't she thought of it in the first place? But why had Basharat said it was someone else? After all, he knew Gurmukh Singh's face from his annual visit.

Sughra went to the front door. There was another knock. Her heart missed a beat. 'Who is it?' she asked in a faint voice.

Basharat whispered to her to look through a small hole in the door.

It wasn't Gurmukh Singh, who was a very old man. This was a young fellow. He knocked again. He was holding a bag in his hand, of the same kind Gurmukh Singh used to bring.

'Who are you?' she asked, a little more confident now.

'I am Sardar Gurmukh Singh's son Santokh.'

Sughra's fear had suddenly gone. 'What brings you here today?' she asked politely.

'Where is judge sahib?' he asked.

'He is not well,' Sughra answered.

'Oh, I'm sorry,' Santokh Singh said. Then he shifted his bag from one hand to the other. 'These are home-made noodles.' Then after a pause, 'Sardarji[3] is dead.'

'Dead!'

'Yes, a month ago, but one of the last things he said to me was, 'For the last ten years, on the occasion of Id, I have always taken my small gift to judge sahib. After I am gone, it will become your duty.' I gave him my word that I would not fail him. I am here today to honour the promise made to my father on his death-bed.'

Sughra was so moved that tears came to her eyes. She opened the door a little. The young man pushed the bag towards her. 'May God rest his soul,' she said.

'Is judge sahib not well?' he asked.

'No.'

'What's wrong?'

'He had a stroke.'

'Had my father been alive, it would have grieved him deeply. He never forgot judge sahib's kindness until his last breath. He used to say, "He is not a man, but a god." May God keep him under his care. Please convey my respects to him.'

He left before Sughra could make up her mind whether or not to ask him to get a doctor.

As Santokh Singh turned the corner, four men, their faces covered with their turbans, moved towards him. Two of them held burning oil torches, the others carried cans of kerosene oil and explosives. One of them asked Santokh, 'Sardar Ji, have you completed your assignment?'

The young man nodded.

'Should we then proceed with ours?' he asked.

'If you like,' he replied and walked away.

---

[3] a respectful way to address a Sikh man.

FREE DINNERS*

By Farrukh Dhondy

Outcomes

Discussion of Issues

Inclusion
Social class
Teacher vs. pupil relationships
Friendship
Uniforms and culture – the hidden curriculum
Planning your future

TB 56

Literacy Work

Text level
Writing in retrospect
Analysing a poem

TB 52 **TB 55**

Sentence Level
Using the language of the street (colloquialisms)

TB 53

Word Level
Powerful imagery – streetwise similes and metaphors

TB 54

*Please note these stories contain strong language.

Stimulus Page

In this story Lorraine, the central character, uses some very colourful language. Some people might find this offensive whilst others would say that it was appropriate in the circumstances. What do you think about hard-hitting language? Should it be allowed on television, for instance? Would you have laws which restrict certain types of language? Discuss this with your partner and share your views with the class.

Lorraine has a very outspoken personality. This causes her some problems. Is it better to speak out when you know something is wrong or to remain silent and protect yourself? Have your say. Discuss this in your pairs.

Can schools influence what we eventually become in life? Are schools necessary? What will schools in the future be like? Discuss whether or not you think schools can actually make a difference or should we abolish them?

All schools need rules to help people to work together productively. Are all the rules absolutely necessary? Choose one of your school rules and debate how useful it is. You might want to extend this into a whole class debate.

Do schools treat pupils on 'free dinners' fairly? Is it very obvious who is on free dinners in your school? Why do you think it might be difficult for people on free dinners in some schools? Discuss with your partner and then begin reading.

FREE DINNERS

By Farrukh Dhondy

Lorraine was in my first-year class at school and the only reason I noticed her was because she was on free dinners like me. We was the only two in that class who had to take the shame of it. We had a right nasty teacher, Mr Cobb, (so you know what we used to call him). Just the way he called your name at the end of the register made you crawl and feel two feet small. He'd collect the money from the other kids and make Lorraine and me queue up separately at his table. Not that he ever said anything to us. He just finished with the regular kids and then announced 'Free Dinners' even though there was only two of us.

After the first week of that, I couldn't take it no more, so I used to go and sit in the bogs when the dinner register was taken and go down to the office after and get my mark. That was dangerous too, 'cos when some wally set fire to the bogs, I got the blame. The register never seemed to bother Lorraine. She would stand up in front of me, and even at that age she looked unconcerned with the way the world treated her. She had a look of thinking about something else all the time, and had tight little lips which showed you that she was right tough and determined – and she was skinny as barbed wire.

She was a coloured kid, or at least she was a half-caste or something like that. We always called them 'coloured' when I first went to school because we didn't think there was nothing wrong with it; but after, some of them would thump you if you called them 'coloured'. They didn't like that, they wanted to be called 'black'. I'm not really sure to this day what she was, on account of never seeing her mum or dad. All the other kids would talk about their mums and dads and the gear they had indoors, but Lorraine always kept herself to herself. She wasn't much to look at and she didn't get on with any of the other girls, because some of the white girls were right snobbish. The other coloured kids would talk black when the teachers weren't there, and they left Lorraine out because she never.

She was good at sports and she was good at drama. I wouldn't have noticed her, I tell you, because at that age I wasn't interested in girls. The other lads would talk about what they done with girls and that, but I couldn't be bothered, and because I was skint till the fourth year, I never took no girls out or even let the kids in the class know who I fancied. It was a girl in our class called Wendy. She had a nasty tongue, but I liked her. I remember the first time Lorraine and I stood in the free dinner queue, Wendy said, 'She looks like she needs them and all.' The other kids laughed, and I must have blushed all over my fat cheeks. Old Cobblers didn't tell Wendy off or have a go at her, and Lorraine just pretended she didn't hear.

I kind of hated Lorraine. I knew that the rest of the class thought that we was tramps. I knew it wasn't her fault, but she was kind of showing me up just by her existence. She wouldn't go and hide in the girls' bogs, she'd just stand there in front of Cobblers' desk and be the only one in the class on free dinners, and because she was there the other kids would know I was hiding, because Cobblers would say, 'Biggs has gone underground again,' or something.

When Lorraine started coming flash the other kids began to take notice of her. In our fifth year she was going to get the drama prize. She was good at acting, and the drama teacher had sent her to some competition which she'd won. She dressed her up as a page boy and gave her a boy's part from Shakespeare. It made her look nice, because she had short hair and sort of squarey shoulders, even though she was as thin as a broomstick. I was the captain of the football team and had to pick up the cup for the team on prize day. The deputy head called all the kids who'd won prizes into the hall and told us that the Bishop would be there to give us our prizes that evening and how we should make sure that our parents came. She went on and on about school uniform and what the boys should wear and how we should wash our hair and have clear hands for the Bishop to shake. Then she turned to the girls and did a right turn, showing them how to curtsy, which made them giggle. Then she goes, 'I've told you this before, but I'll rehearse it with you again. You won't be allowed to accept any prize unless you're decently dressed, and that means school uniform. If you don't have one, you'll have to get a skirt below the knee, a clean white blouse and blue cardigan. And no blue and green tights. I want all the girls to wear flesh-coloured tights.'

'Whose flesh, miss?' Lorraine asked.

The deputy head stopped as though Lorraine had clocked her one. Some of the girls giggled.

'Go and wait outside the hall for me, will you, Lorraine?' she said quietly, and Lorraine walked out, saying, 'I only asked a simple question,' and she knew that at least a few admiring eyes were following her.

It was the first time I had heard Lorraine say anything coloured, anything to show that she knew she was coloured. I'll tell you straight up, that if anyone else had said that, I would have thought it was too flash. The coloured kids in our year were a load of wankers. They didn't want to mix with the rest of us. When they had a laugh it was on their own, and they collected together in the fifth-year room at lunch times and after school and took over the record player and just played their dub and reggae and that. Some of them were all right, but some of them just liked to come flash with you.

When we gathered that evening in room B12, behind the stage, waiting to get the prizes, Lorraine walked in looking a real state. She had on black velvet hot-pants and a black silk shirt and had made herself up to look right tarty with crimson lipstick and heavy eyeshadow. The girls sort of turned away when she came in and the boys started making remarks and whistling to take the piss and I was looking, just staring at her because she didn't half look different, dressed like that. Then the deputy came in and threw a fit. Her jaw dropped down to her tits. She rushed Lorraine out of the room and we all ran to the door to hear them arguing in the corridor.

The deputy was telling her that she could still get her prize if she'd wash her face and change into a spare skirt and blouse that she'd give her. But Lorraine wasn't having it. It was as if she'd turned beastly at sunset or something. She gave the deputy some nasty cheek and the deputy didn't turn the other one, she just tried to tell her to 'clear off the premises', and Lorraine said she'd wear what she liked out of school time because it was her culture, and the deputy said she was still in school time if she was inside the gates. When the deputy came back in our room, she was sort of blinking to hold back her tears, looking like Lorraine had really told her which stop to get off at. Lorraine didn't collect the prize of course.

It was after that prize day that Lorraine became a bit of a loud mouth. I heard her telling some of the coloured kids that the deputy head was jealous of her and prejudiced, and didn't want her to be an actress, and wanted to shove her off to work in a laundry. And Lorraine took her revenge.

We were in the maths class and the deputy came in and put her coffee mug, which she always carried around the corridors of the school, down on the teacher's desk. She asked the teacher's permission and began telling us about some fight on a bus in which our kids had duffed up the conductor or something. Everyone was listening quietly and Lorraine, pretending to talk to another girl, said, 'I bet she'll blame the blacks.' The deputy didn't pay any attention, just finished what she was saying and then asked the maths teacher if she could have a word with him outside. She was a bit put out, so she left her coffee on the desk and went out with him.

When they stepped out, Lorraine got up from her desk and went to the front of the class and looked in the coffee cup. We thought she'd take a drink and some kids said, 'Go on, dare you.' So Lorraine turns to the class and says,

'What, drink *her* coffee, and get rabies?' and she cleared her throat with a loud hawking sound and gobbed into the cup, a huge slimy gob. She stirred it with her pencil and without a smile to the rest of the class, sat down again. The two teachers came back in the room and the deputy took her coffee and split. The maths geezer said that Lorraine was to report to the Head's office at 12.30. Lorraine said, 'Yes, sir,' and the maths feller said, 'You ought to be given a taste of your own rudeness.' The kids all laughed and he didn't know why.

It was at that time I think that I began to admire Lorraine. I told myself that if I got the chance I'd ask her out, but I didn't want any of the lads to know what was on my mind because, for one, they didn't ever take black girls out, not the mob I moved with in school and, for another, they thought Lorraine was some kind of looney loner. That's why I didn't ask her to the fifth-year dance, and good job I didn't, because she came to the dance with a group of black boys from Brixton and they pushed past the teachers at the door and began to act like they owned the place. I think Lorraine just brought them to show that she moved with the dread locks or whatever they liked to call themselves. It wasn't going to be a particularly good party with no booze or nothing.

These kids brought their own records and they broke up the dance when they started threatening the guy who was playing DJ for the evening. The guy stopped the music and the teachers switched all the bright lights on and suddenly the place was full of teachers and schoolkeepers, and when Lorraine's crowd started arguing back, they called the police. A lot of the white kids began to drift off, because a blind man could see there was going to be trouble.

I was watching Lorraine. She looked as though she knew she had gone too far. She was trying to cool it and reason with her black friends, but they shoved her aside and shaped up like they were going to duff up the DJ. Then someone said the police had arrived outside and the black kids legged it. Lorraine got into a lot of trouble on account of that scene. Some of the kids, the next day, the white kids, were talking as though they were scared of Lorraine. The blacks were laughing about it. Lorraine wasn't laughing with them; she was just pretending she hadn't been there and getting on with her classwork. That's what I liked about her. She created hell and behaved as though she was the angel of the morning.

At this time I was going out with Wendy. She was right hard, harder than a gob-stopper, and she always settled arguments with her fists. I suppose I was a bit fed up of her really. She never let me touch her all the time we was going out. She was a bit of a tom-boy and didn't even want to be kissed. Her dad was a copper and strict. I had to take Wendy home at eleven even if we went to a party. I was fair sick of her, even though she was a good-looker, nice face, big tits and always dressed flash.

I wanted to ask Lorraine out and I knew that Wendy would do her nut if she found out. I brought up the subject once with the lads I used to circulate with, and they figured that Lorraine was right easy, that she'd let you do anything with her. They said the black guys from Brixton whom she went out with wouldn't hang around her for nothing. They figured she wouldn't go out with a white bloke. I didn't say nothing to them, but one day after school when I knew she had drama club, I waited around in the year-room and played records till the other kids had gone home and started chatting her up.

I was quite surprised when she said she'd go to the pictures with me. We fixed it for the next time she was staying late at school. I didn't tell the lads in school about our date, but I phoned my friend Tony, who lived in his own flat and told him that I might drop in for a bit after the pictures if my bird fancied staying out. I had six quid on me that day. I met Lorraine up the Elephant in the evening and I said I wanted to go to the Swedish movies, they were really good, but she laughed at me and took me to some crummy film about some stripper girl in Germany or some place.

Lorraine didn't talk silly like Wendy. She had sort of two sides to her. She was a bit posh and she was also hard black. She'd go to the pictures that snobs would see, and she'd want to go to plays and things, and then she'd also talk rude and swear in Jamaican and that.

Until I took her out, I never knew she talked so much. She was explaining the film to me. It was nice listening to her. She wasn't thick like Wendy. When she started explaining why the stripper done what she done, it was nice. It was like I'd had six pints and all the words made sense to me, or like I didn't care if they made sense or not, there was something new and exciting about them.

Then after the pictures I asked her if she fancied going down to my friend's place, because he might be having a party and she gave me a smile and said she was hungry.

'Fancy some chips?' I asked.

'I'm going to take you out to a meal, Peter,' she said.

That touched me. It fair knocked me out, to tell you the truth. We went to this Chinese joint she knew in the West End. She was putting on the style, but I didn't mind.

When we sat down they brought this tea that smelt like bad after-shave. She started pouring it out and knocking it back and I said I couldn't drink tea without milk and three teaspoons of sugar and she laughed.

'What do you want to eat, Pete?' she asked. 'Don't worry, I'll pay.'

'I'll have a plaice and chips.' I said, not looking at the menu.

'Don't be so thick, 'darling',' she said, pronouncing the 'darling' like one of the girls in the film we'd just seen.

'Steak and chips, then,' I said.

'You can stop playing Cockney hero now,' she said.

'I ain't eating no ying yang food,' I said.

She just grabbed the menu from my hand and went into splits. She split herself, and on my mother's life I couldn't see the joke, so I said I wasn't hungry, but to tell you the truth my stomach was growling like a waterfall.

I sat and watched as she swallowed all the spaghetti and stuff. She kept saying I ought to try some, but I wasn't going to show myself up. If I'd said one thing, then I was going to stick to it. 'I'm not hungry,' I said.

When I left her at the bus-stop she asked me if I'd enjoyed my dinner. Real flippin' cheeky she was.

'Best portion of plaice and chips I've had in years, really crisp,' I said, just to show I didn't have any hard feelings, even though my feelings were harder than exams. I'd paid for the dinner. I'd insisted.

'I've always enjoyed free dinners,' she said, as she got on the 133 to Brixton from the Elephant. That's the kind of brass you don't need to polish, I thought, as I walked back home with my hands in my pockets.

I rang up Tony and told him it didn't work out. I tried to take Wendy out again, but she was going with this geezer from Scotland Yard who had a blue Cortina and she told me she didn't want to go out with schoolboys. I'd have asked Lorraine out again, but I felt she was only tolerating me and she didn't fancy me one bit. I thought about her a lot. She was a funny girl. I didn't speak to her in school after that evening. I don't know what it was, I can't quite put my finger on it, but I felt she was telling me somehow to keep my distance. When I was going with Wendy, I always got the feeling that she'd do her nut if I packed her in, but with Lorraine it was like she expected nothing, wanted nothing, she'd take what came, and wait for more to come.

Then she started taking the mick. It was in a General Studies class in the sixth form, and this teacher was going on about why the Irish were thick or something. He was saying that everybody thought that everybody else was thick, that it was natural, and if the British thought the Irish were not so smart, then the Jews thought the British were not so smart and the Americans thought that the British were all snobs or all Cockneys talked in rhyming slang and the like. Then Lorraine started shooting her mouth. There was only twelve of us in that class and we sat around a table in the sixth-form suite and this geezer never stopped talking about politics and racial relations and prejudice and all that crap. Lorraine always talked to him like she was the only one in the class and we was out in the playground playing marbles and she was on telly.

'That's what all white people think,' she said. 'It's just stupidity. They think Pakis are all Oxfam and niggers live in trees, and Chinese food is ying yang food.'

I knew she was getting at me. Then the geezer asked us for our views, so I said, 'I reckon that a lot of it is true, that blacks do live off Social Security, because there's a black feller on our estate and he drives a Benz, and polishes it up every Saturday and when you see him he's always got a new suit and he goes with white slags, a new one every two hours, and he never works. It's nothing to do with prejudice, it's just that a lot of white people pay a lot of tax and rates and that the blacks come in and take Social Security . . .'

'And eat a lot of free dinners,' Lorraine said.

She was a bitch. She never talked to me after that. Not till we left school.

I'd meet someone from school down the Walworth Road and they'd say, 'Watcha, Pete,' and we'd have a talk. I wanted to be an architect, but I had to get my City and Guilds Draughtsman's exams first, so I was working with this firm on an apprenticeship. We'd talk about this and that and how much lolly we was taking home and about the old teachers and the old times. All the white kids I met from school knew Wendy had gone for an Old Bill, and she was saying 'hello, hello, hello' instead of 'watcha'. We didn't talk about the black kids, except for Keith, who wasn't like the rest of them and was trying to be a draughtsman himself. If I saw any of the blacks I'd been in school with, they would raise their hands, or just blank me, and we'd pass without a word. I though a bit about Lorraine. If I met her again, I told myself, I'd ask her out, show her that I'd learnt a thing or two, I'd planned it all out in my head. We'd go to the same cinema and see some posh movie or other, whatever was running, and then I'd take her to a Chinese and order a Won-ton Soup and Crab in Ginger, Char Si Pong, the lot, just to show her that old Pete had learnt a thing or two with the lads at the firm who were fond of a curry or of a Chinese or pizza after a hard Friday night's drinking down the local. The lads would talk about a Vindaloo and a Madras as though they was bloody veterans of the Burmese campaign.

When I actually met her, there was no chance. Well, I didn't exactly meet her. I just saw her and we exchanged a few words. It was like this. I was round Kilburn way, 'cos our office has a branch up there, and I was told to go and discuss some designs with a top geezer in our firm who worked in Kilburn. The lads from the Kilburn office sussed me out and, after, we went for a drink in a pub round their way. I didn't know them much, but I strung along.

The pub was a young scene, Friday night boppers from round the top end of the Edgeware Road. There were lights popping all over the ceiling and huge mirrors on the walls which were otherwise plastered with old newspapers to give the place the look of being in the know. Up the end of the bar was this geezer doing the disco, leaning over his tube microphone and running down the soul.

'We're gonna have some dancing in a piece, Pete,' Sol told me. 'This is a nice scene, topless go-go, strippers, a pint of real ale, a real good time.'

So the spotlight came on the stage and the disco geezer introduced the dancer. We were at the bar. A few of the lads had grabbed stools and I was standing with my pint with my back to the stage and the dance floor. When the music stopped I looked around. You could have knocked me down with a feather. Just outside the circle of the spotlight, like a ghost, like a bloody shivering ghost, stood Lorraine, in a dressing-gown which she was urging off her shoulders. Some black guy was waiting at the corner of the stage to catch it as it dropped. As the DJ finished his introduction, she strolled into the light in heels and gold knickers with purple tassles dangling from them and no bra. The pub had turned its attention to her, though I could see that the fellers in my mob were pretending to take it cool.

They were all screwing her and giving off that they weren't
interested at all.

The strobe came on and the green and blue lights began
flashing. Lorraine with her haunted face and wiry body began
her dance, her skinny pair of legs like those of a delicate race-
horse, slim, with the muscles running on the bone, shifting with
some hesitance.

'I heard it through the grapevine, no longer will you be mine,'
sang Marvin Gaye, and the mob I was with began to hoot and
clap.

'Look at the fucking state of it,' said Sol. 'Blimey, I'd rather
go to Madame Tussaud's and see the Chamber of Horrors.'

In the dark she couldn't see us, she couldn't have known
where the voices were coming from. Between the stage and us
there were these pillars, and I felt like disappearing behind one
of them. She was dancing good, mind you, but it was true that
she didn't have much meat on her.

She was a mover, give her that. And she had some guts, getting
up in front of that mob and doing her thing.

'Oxfam,' one of the lads shouted, and the faces in the darkness
tittered.

'Spare ribs,' Sol shouted, as she danced on.

'Knock it off,' I said. 'Don't show us up.'

'Spare ribs,' someone else shouted from the far end of the
pub. She had small breasts, flat on her sinewy body. Of course
she heard the voices, heard the laughter, but her expression
didn't change. She was dancing for all her worth, and her body
moved gracefully through the tune, but there was no sex in it, if
you know what I mean. She wasn't no topless dancer, and if she
didn't realize it, the governor of the pub should've.

'Spare ribs.' They'd picked it up at the other end of the pub
and were trying to give her the slow hand-clap. They were going
at it like it was the first laugh they'd had that week.

The record finished and Lorraine stepped hastily out of the
spotlight. The DJ quickly flipped turntables and started some
soul sounds. I watched her as her man gave her the dressing-
gown and she rushed to the ladies.

'The gaffer's not going to have her again,' the barman said.

I left my pint on the bar and waited till she came out of the
ladies. She was wearing a trouser suit and a band around her
forehead. As I approached her I could see her mascara was

smudged and she looked like she'd rather be on the Flying Scotsman to hell than right there in that pub. She was in a hurry, but she saw me and recognized me.

'Hello, Lorraine,' I said, not knowing what else to say. I felt the lads had treated her something rotten, something shameful, and on my life if I'd been able to, I would have got them publicly on their knees to her.

She was as surprised as I was.

'I didn't know you hung around my ex-beat,' she said.

'I didn't know you'd started professional dancing,' I said.

'Well, you heard what the customers thought,' she said.

'They're a load of stupid fuckers,' I said. 'Excuse the language. How're you getting on?'

I wanted to ask her for a drink, but it was the wrong place, the wrong moment. I wanted to tell her that I'd often thought of her, that now more than ever I wondered where she'd got to, what she was doing, how she kept herself. Her man come up and touched her elbow.

'I'll see you, Pete,' she said.

'Yeah,' I said.

'I'm dancing in another pub,' she said. 'Half an hour. Rough stuff, this, earning your dinners,' and she smiled and walked away. I went back to my pint.

The last time I saw her was very brief. I met her on the pavement in Soho. It was raining. I'd finished my time at the firm and I'd bought this car and dropped my mate and girl-friend off at Gerrard Street. I'd gone to park the car. I saw her coming from a few yards down. She was with an old bald geezer in a posh raincoat. She was hanging on to his arm, dressed to the hilt, made up like a wedding cake. She looked stoned, too, unsteady on her feet.

'I saw you first this time,' she said.

She stopped in front of me and smiled, and her mouth opened but her eyes stayed distant, like I'd known them, like they were when she was thinking of other things when we'd been there, children in the first year of school. The old man stood a little way behind her and she behaved as though he wasn't there. She put her fingers on my tie, and said, 'How are you, Pete?'

I stepped back a bit.

'I'm just going to see some friends,' I said.

'Have you seen anyone from the old school?' she asked. 'I haven't seen any of them bastards,' she added, veering on her feet.

'No, no, I haven't,' I said.

'Oh, hang on,' she said. 'I saw your girl-friend Wendy. You know what she said to me?'

'Yes, Wendy,' I said. 'She's in the police, isn't she?'

'She too damn feisty. She catch me on my business,' Lorraine said, her accent suddenly becoming black.

'Oh, oh,' I said. 'You been nicking from Woolworth's again, Lorraine?'

I shuffled my feet. I could see it coming.

'You see this, Pete,' Lorraine said, taking on step back and pointing with a flowing hand at the pavement. 'This here is the street. Your Wendy don't want me to walk the street and she is a po-lis.' She nodded. Now I could see that she was drunk, but her eyes which stared into mine looked sober as the rising sun. 'She don't like me walk the street, our Wendy,' she said.

'Yes,' I said. 'What do you expect from the Old Bill? She wasn't ever my girl, Lorraine!'

'You want to get out of the rain, Pete,' she said. She began to walk past me dragging the old geezer after her.

'Pete,' she said, and turned round as though she'd forgotten something. 'Pete, I'll see yuh.' She was facing me again and she turned to the old geezer who looked impatient to shove off. 'It's Pete, my old school mate. Pete, this is Mr Smith who's just going to buy me a free dinner.'

WAR OF THE WORLDS*

By Ravinder Randhawa

Outcomes

Discussion of Issues

Stating your case – standing up for what you believe
Conflict – parents and children
Girl Power

TB 59

Literacy Work

Text level
Structuring stories – using the 'flashback' technique
Writing to protest

TB 58 **TB 61**

Sentence Level
Using imagery

TB 60

Drama and oral activities

Reactions from the crowd – role play of the meeting
Speaking out – how to protest

TB 61

*Please note these stories contain strong language.

Stimulus Page

The title of this story is very similar to another famous book. Find out which one, and then collect some information about the story, its plot and main ideas.

The word 'Gurudwara' is used several times in this story. Some of you will know that this is the place of worship for Sikhs. It is the place where congregations are held.

The story begins with an angry parent, expressing her views to her two daughters. What do you think might be the reasons for her anger?

If you were given the opportunity to express your views about something in front of a group of adults, what would you choose to say? What would you like to complain about, or try to change?

As the story begins, notice how the writer plunges you right into the middle of the argument. You will gradually begin to realise what has been happening and why the mother is so angry . . .

WAR OF THE WORLDS

By Ravinder Randhawa

'You two want to do what you want? Behave as you please?' Mum's voice hard and strained, refusing to shed the tears flooding her eyes. 'If you don't like living here, you can leave. Both of you.' It was like being given ECT. Little shockwaves burned through us. I could see Suki's eyes growing larger and larger, expanding exponentially. Mum had never said anything like this to us before.

She'd never blamed us before, she'd blamed the nurse in the hospital when we were born. 'Twin daughters' she'd told Mum, bearing one on each arm. 'Aren't they sweet? Sweet on the outside, acid on the inside,' she'd said sing-song. 'Oh, they're going to be terrible. The Terrible Twins!' chuckling away.

'Because your father isn't around any more . . .' Mum still couldn't bring herself to use words like dead . . . 'you think you no longer need to watch your tongue, or have respect for other people. And you never have to come back. Have your freedom.' Scooping up the baby, marching off upstairs.

It wasn't that we'd changed, things had. We'd been wilder than wild even when Dad was alive: running round town like we were urban guerrillas of the Asian kind. No part of town we didn't know, no person we didn't suss out, no action we didn't know about. The town was our battleground. Our Frontline. Dad would rave and rant at us, tell us we were shameless, not fit to live in civilised society and did we know what happened to women like us? Dad wanted us to be accommodating, to fit in, to live like decent people. We know what 'decent' people get up to when they think no one's looking, we argued back, like there seems to be one set of rules people use if they think they're going to be found out and another set if they think they can do whatever they want in safe secrecy. And it's not as if everyone doesn't know what's going on. They're all happy to shut their eyes to it 'cos they don't want to rock the boat and they don't want to grass on anyone else in case they get grassed on themselves.

Mum and Dad copped it from us every time. We were part of them and they were part of us and that's why we could never be soft with them. If we got them to agree with us, just once, it was like the gates were opened for us to take on the whole world.

And now Mum was saying we could leave. Go. Do what we want. Walk out the front door. We both swivelled our heads to look towards it, though of course we couldn't see it from where we were sitting. Suki and I didn't look at each other; we didn't have to. Mum's ultimatum was ticking like a time-bomb in our brains.

Freedom!

We both stood up, went towards the front door and opened it. It was a beautiful summer evening: balmy, cool, fragrant. Real tourist brochure stuff. We stepped out, over the threshold.

'Charlie's having her party tonight,' said Suki.

'Probably be the same old crowd.'

'We should go to London. Thousands of new people there.'

'Millions. And new things to do.'

'Living on our own.'

'Making it in the Metropolis.'

A car drove by and the bloke in it waved to us. We both waved back, our arms like enthusiastic windscreen wipers. We could hear him reversing his car further up the road, the gravel crunching under his tyres. The blokes loved doing that. Made them feel like Action Man come alive. His engine noise zoomed towards us and then stopped as the car came to a body-shaking, gravel-crunching stop outside our gate.

'You gonna go?' asked Suki.

'I did him last time. He won't know the difference.'

She sauntered off towards him and I sat peeling grass blades, till a pile of curled green strips lay at my feet.

Their voices rose and fell, scraps of sentences floated back to me followed by occasional riffs of laughter; Suki was leading him on, making him think he had a chance. He didn't of course. He was too ordinary. His flash car and trendy clothes couldn't make up for the mediocre stuff in his brain. I was surprised he hadn't heard of us, hadn't been warned off going near the terrible twins. We had a whole pack of enemies in town, not least among them, the blokes who'd sworn they loved us madly and couldn't live without us. Until we put our reject stamp on them.

Suki and I always compared notes and it was always the same old story: unimaginative, unintelligent. Men who thought they were God's special gift to Asian women. The white blokes wanted to liberate us from our 'primitive' traditions and customs; the Asian blokes thought weren't we lucky to be loved by them in spite of our dubious reputations and bad style of life. Nothing guaranteed to make us run faster and further than blokes imagining themselves to be 'In Love' with us. We'd seen enough of the after-effects of 'In Love' to make us avoid it like the proverbial plague.

First there was Janet, whose bloke had been 'In Love' with her, had chased her for months till she'd finally come round, as they say; come to her senses, he'd said. And Paul had been ever so romantic, insisting on a church wedding, white dress, whisking her off to a grand honeymoon. Janet don't talk about Love no more though – bit difficult when half your teeth been knocked out, and all the other bits of your body knocked in.

Then there was our cousin, Jeeta. Got to be fair, he hadn't said he loved Kulwinder. Just that he forgot to tell her that he'd promised his love to the *gori* next door; just that he didn't have the guts to tell his mother, either, as she busily went about arranging his marriage to Kulwinder. Kulwinder who was sweet, obedient and modest, the perfect Indian girl, the perfect Indian bride.

'Being perfect didn't stop her getting messed up, did it?' said Suki in one of her sarky moods.

Kulwinder did her best. We know she tried hard, but she was too innocent, too simple for his tactics, and he knew she didn't know how to fight back. He wanted to drive her away by driving her to a nervous breakdown; that much she sussed out and flew the nest before the rot could set in.

Suki and I couldn't believe it. The whole family, even our

Mum and Dad, sided with him: they said she should have tried harder, been more patient, understanding. Marriage wasn't the easy option the West made it out to be. It had to be worked at, sacrifices and compromises made. 'Sita-Savitri doesn't live here any more, don't you know?' I said. Wasted my inter-cultural mythical allusions, didn't I, 'cos they all turned round and looked as blank as blank at me.

Suki and I wanted to make Halal meat out of Jeeta and serve him up to Kulwinder on a platter, but she wouldn't have none of it. She was too good an Indian girl to get mixed up in revenge and justice, and anyway her father had to think of her future. He'd have to start looking for another marriage for her. She mustn't jeopardise her chances.

Then there was the time we brought Shanti and her baby home.

'They've been thrown out of their home, Mum, and an English woman was trying to help her, but you know how none of these *goras* can speak Punjabi . . .'

'Illiterate lot,' added Suki, interrupting my grand speech. Mum took her in and Mum and Mum's friends all gathered round to help. They brought clothes for Shanti and the baby, they cooked food for them, they condoled, they consoled, they commiserated and then stood back as Shanti and baby went back to her horrible husband. We couldn't understand it and attacked Mum for driving her back.

'Shanti thought it over and made her own choice,' said Mum.

'Some choice,' muttered Suki.

'That's all some women get.'

'It's wrong.'

'Yes,' replied Mum, seeming to agree with us for once, 'but it won't be for long, will it? You are going to change the world, aren't you?' She could be dead sarcastic, our mum.

We couldn't let it go, could we? We decided on direct action: decided to get them at the Gurudwara. Anyone could get up and speak. The men did it all the time, giving long lectures on righteous living and long-winded explanations of God's thoughts and intentions; they all talked like they had a hot line to the heavens.

We'd made sure we were dressed proper and started off by reading a verse from Suki's *Gotka* (no, she hadn't got religion, just thought it was 'bootiful' poetic stuff. Mum and Dad would get ever so pleased when they saw her reading it – thinking that the light of goodness had finally touched their wayward daughter). I've done a lot of things in my (short) life, but getting up there in front of all them Sunday-come-to-worship-people was the toughest. It started off all sweet and nice, the mothers and grandmothers smiling at us, whispering among themselves about how nice it was to see us young women taking part. I sneaked a glance at Dad. Shouldn't have. His eyes were sending out laser beams of anger. He knew we were up to something.

Finishing the verse, we started in on our talk, speaking our best Punjabi and careful not to let our dupattas slip off our heads. We began by saying that there was much suffering in our community and that we, as the Gurudwara, should organise to do something about it. For instance there should be a fund for women who have to leave home because they are being beaten or ill-treated; the Gurudwara should arrange accommodation as well as helping them with education and training and make sure they weren't outcast by the rest of the community. Rather the Gurudwara should praise them for having the courage to liberate themselves from cruelty, just as India had liberated herself from the cruelty of the Raj (rather a neat touch, I thought: the linking of the personal to the political, the micro to the macro). It was as if the windows had banged open and let in a hot strong wind; a susurration of whisper eddied to and fro.

They didn't know we'd only given them the hors d'oeuvre. We then suggested that the problem should be tackled at the root: men were not going to have respect for women unless they had respect for women's work; therefore the boys should be taught cooking, cleaning, babycare, etc. The men sniggered, some laughed out loud.

'Men who beat or mistreat their wives should be heavily fined by the Gurudwara, and if they persist should be cast out from our society. And if they've taken a dowry they should be made to return it, in double. Blokes who make girls pregnant and then leave them in the lurch should never be allowed to have an arranged marriage . . .' We had to stop 'cos Pati's dad, Harcharan Singh, stood up and launched into an attack on us. We were really disgusted! That man spent more money on his drinking and smoking than he did on his family, and still wanted them to be grateful for whatever scraps he threw their way. This man was now standing up and accusing us of being corrupt and dangerous; others were nodding their heads in agreement.

'Are you saying these things don't happen?' we asked, all innocent-like.

I don't think he even heard, just carried on with his diatribe against 'children who don't know their place and women who have no respect for tradition and custom.' Others couldn't wait and interrupted until there were several voices all speaking at once. One voice strained above the others and accused us of bringing dirt and filth into the house of God and getting a bit carried away he let slip a couple of nasty words. Mistake, because Mrs Gill, who was a Moral Majority in her own right, got up immediately and rounded on him like a 40-ton truck. Adjusting her dupatta like a gunslinger adjusting his holster, she told him it was his rotten tongue defiling the house of God and why couldn't the men sit quiet and let the girls finish what they were saying.

'We should listen to our young sometimes,' she said. 'We may learn something.' She gave us the all-clear nod and sat back down among the women.

This was the crunch, the lunge for the jugular vein, and as I formed the words and reached for the microphone I found my voice, Suki's voice, reaching out, spreading across the hall: 'It's no good coming to the Gurudwara once a week to show how clean and pure you are, it doesn't hide all the sordid, underhand things that have been happening all week. The Gurudwara isn't the disinfectant that kills 99 per cent of all germs. It should be treated with more respect. In turn we who are the Gurudwara should get tough on those men who harass us women, whistle at us, touch us up, attempt to force us into their cars . . . Some of them are sitting right here and they know who they are.' Like a storm among the trees angry, aggrieved whispers were rustling around the men . . . 'What about the man who's started a prostitution racket? He's here. And those who can't tell the difference between their daughters and their wives . . .' The place exploded, most rising to their feet, some raising their fists to us, others moving forward, pushing through towards us.

Dad had saved us. Defused the anger. The crowd had parted to let him through.

'I suppose we'll have to call him Moses after this,' whispered Suki. He stopped by us and turned round to face the others.

'It's late. I'm going to take my daughters home. But we can't go without having Prasad.' Picking up the covered bowl of warm Prasad Dad served us each with a round ball of the gorgeous delicious sweet, whispering to us to meet him by the car. He turned round and started serving those nearest to us. Prasad is God's food and you're not supposed to refuse it. You should be glad it's offered to you.

'D-a-d is O-u-r C-h-a-m-p-i-o-n.' All the way home we wanted to chant 'D-a-d is O-u-r C-h-a-m-p-i-o-n,' like the football fans do, but he was in a foul mood so we shut up and kept quiet.

'We think what you did was really brave,' said Preeti during the dinner break at school.

'Yeah. Those things really needed to be said,' added Bhupinder, her short pigtails swishing round her face; she never had been able to grow her hair below shoulder length, despite all the creams and lotions she poured on to it.

'So why didn't you say anything?' asked Suki. 'We could have used some help.'

'You kidding? Mum would have come down on me like Two Tons of Bricks.'

'Gutless goons always want other people to do their fighting for them,' I said, hoping it sounded as sarky as I felt.

'No-one asked you to do it,' put in Preeti, coming to her best friend's aid. 'Anyway you two fancy yourselves as Revolutionaries.'

'Freedom Fighters,' added stupid Bhupinder with a stupid giggle. 'We wouldn't want to take your glory from you.'

'And not everyone's got liberal parents like yours.' Poison Preeti again.

Liberal parents! That sure was history, what with Mum as good as throwing us out of the house! Suki was trying to say goodbye to the thing at the gate, his arms stretching out to hold her back, impress her with his burning passion. She moved back towards him once, twice, and I thought, this is silly, why's she wasting her time on him when we've got to talk and make decisions?

'You were right. He's a dead loss.' Her skirt swished by me as she sat down.

'There must be some who aren't.'

'We'll have to go looking for them, won't we?'

'Mum doesn't want us here if we don't change.'

'You want to leave?' Suki turned round to look at me, face on, full frontal.

'I'm not scared of leaving.'

'Not the point.'

'There's always white people and white society . . .?' My voice sounded as if posing a maths problem.

'They'll want us to change to their ways . . .' Suki came back as sharp as a knife.

Silence between the two of us. For a change! I picked up the shredded bits of grass and shifted them through my fingers. 'Not much choice, is there? I guess it's a case of Here to Stay–Here to Fight.'

Suki giggled. 'Old slogans never die, eh?'

I had an idea. I thought it was brilliant. 'Let's go to Patel's.' Suki caught on as I knew she would. 'And see if he's got any mangoes for Mum? Right.'

We closed the gate very carefully behind us, in case Mum heard and wondered.

UPROAR*

By Paul Wong (now called Paul Wu)

Outcomes

Discussion of Issues

Bullying
Tolerance and intolerance
Understanding one another's feelings

TB 66   TB 67

Literacy Work

Text level
Studying themes
Studying characters

TB 66   TB 67   TB 65

Sentence Level
Using the present tense
Simple and complex sentences

TB 63   TB 64

Word Level
Words for feelings

Drama and Oral activities

Hot-seating characters
Circle of whispers – retelling the events
Role play – the aftermath

TB 65

*Please note these stories contain strong language.

Stimulus Page

It has been said that everyone experiences some bullying behaviour from other people at some time in their lives. Do you agree with this statement?

Think about the first trip you went on that meant you would be away from home overnight without your parents or guardians. What were your feelings about it before you went? List the words that best describe these feelings.

As you read the story, look out for the way the writer describes feelings and thoughts. Is there anything you can relate to, that you have also experienced?

There is some very strong language in this story and you need to know this so that, as you read, you can decide whether it was necessary in the context of the story. Discuss with a partner why you think writers sometimes decide to use it.

The boy who tells the story is very honest about himself and about everything that goes wrong. Look out for examples of this from the first sentence . . .

UPROAR

By Paul Wong (now called Paul Wu)

It takes an entire morning for my family to prepare for my first trip away from home. My mother packs all my warm clothes in my small blue suitcase. All the hand-knitted jumpers are in there squashed up against each other. I've put some comics in the suitcase too and my slippers: my blue and white rubber flip-flops. My father brings me a box of roast meats to take along: cha sui pork and roast duck wrapped in opaque plastic, sitting smelling sweet in the cardboard box. I'm not nervous, I'm quite blasé in fact. I've always taken things in my stride: what's all the fuss about. I'm only going away for a week. I'm the only child and it's never dawned on me how important I am to my parents.

I carry the box of roasted meats in a carrier bag and take an orange from my mother and put it into a small duffle bag which I sling over my shoulder. My father takes my case to the car. We're going to be late, we're always late, I kiss my mother goodbye. She sheds a tear and her black eyeliner runs. My father drives like a maniac to my school. He swears at the other drivers, calling them white morons and black monkeys, depending on their race. We arrive at the school gates. The coach is waiting. I'm not the only one who's late. I kiss my father goodbye on his fleshy lips, grab my suitcase and run for the coach. I see the other kids looking out from the windows as the driver loads my suitcase into the underbelly of the coach. I keep hold of my duffle bag and the carrier bag with the box of roast meats in it.

There aren't many seats left so I get to sit with the rowdy kids at the back of the coach. I try to be hard and cool, but I look all wrong. My hair doesn't tousle in the right way and I'm just too much of a swot. I end up sitting in the middle space of the back seat of the bus, the one that goes right along the width of the coach, the red and black velour getting hot over the engine. I clutch my bags on my lap, the box of roast meats on top of the duffle bag. The kids around me ignore me and talk about football matches they've been to and their favourite footballers. I've never watched a football match. My father thinks it's a sport for hooligans and Neanderthals, and I believe him. I've seen the crowds of skinheads flooding the street when a match is on.

It's a long coach journey, and I begin to feel a bit ill. My stomach is churning and the heat of the engine is searing into my bottom. I squirm in the seat as the other boys begin tucking into packets of crisps and reading football magazines and boring English comics. My nausea gets worse as the boy on my right starts talking to me, his breath stinking of cheese and onion flavour crisps and cola. He asks me if I'm from Hong Kong, because he knows a boy from the local take-away who was born in Hong Kong. I tell him that I was born in Britain. I guess I must sound really snooty but I really don't want to be associated with those Fried-ricers the Hong Kongers. The boy tells me that this Hong Kong boy is a good footballer. They play on the common at weekends. As he says this he stuffs more crisps into his mouth and then slurps some cola. I feel strange about him telling me this – I've never played football on the common, except with my father or my cousins. Somehow I never really mixed with the other boys.

The boy on my left, Daniel, asks me what I've got in my bags. I tell him it's cha sui pork, my favourite food. He tells me his favourite is macaroni cheese, but I tell him nothing compares to cha sui pork. He asks for a bit, he wants to try some. I like Daniel, he's a rough diamond, he's Jewish and is always talking about his family – how his mother beat him up but now he didn't care and only pretended to cry to make her stop and feel so bad she'd spoil him and give him whatever he wanted. He prefers fighting to football and has a gap in his front teeth, but he's never picked on me. He's always let me be.

I open up the carrier bag and then the box, the sweet barbecue smell explodes in my face and I tear open the plastic and dig out a piece of cold cha sui pork for Daniel. He takes it and chews it. He thinks about it and proclaims it to be not bad. I offer a piece to the cheese and onion kid on my right, and he too approves of a small piece of cha sui pork, saying that he'd tried something similar from his local take-away. Then a boy sitting ahead of me turns around. It's Jan. A small gypsy-ish looking boy, Jan's a tough nut, a hard boy, a bully. He complains about the smell, says it smells like shit and it must be coming from me: 'the chink'. I close the box and tie the handles of the carrier bag into a knot. Daniel yells to Jan that I've got some roast meats, and that they taste really good. Jan swears at Daniel and calls him Jewboy and laughs with his mates. One of the teachers stands up and tells the back of the coach to keep the noise down. The engine heat burns into my backside and I see Jan look round at me and laugh.

We arrive at the camp and I wait until everyone has gone off the coach before I get off. We stand in file and get allocated our huts. The air smells of countryside: slightly damp and green somehow. I carry my suitcase and bags to the hut along with most of the other boys. We put our cases on shelves just before we enter the dormitory. There are two lines of bunk beds and the rest of the boys run to claim their beds near to their friends. I get to share a bunk bed with Paul, a studious and quiet Indian boy. He gets the top bunk and I get the bottom. We're civil to one another, as if we belong to the same club somehow but we haven't ever really talked.

I take out my pyjamas and place then under the pillow and take my new wash bag from my duffle bag, and place it on the bed along with a large orange towel. We've got half an hour before dinner, so I get out my comic books and lie on top of my bed and read them: the X-Men, Superman, The Legion of Super-Heroes. I immerse myself in these brightly coloured panels, where people could fly and everyone was different, had different powers and different costumes but were happy together fighting against common enemies, making a difference. The other boys milled around, larking about, whipping each other with towels and bouncing a football from bed to bed, but I was oblivious to it all.

Dinner comes and goes, I eat the boiled cabbage and the tapioca pudding, thinking about the box of roast meats in my suitcase. After dinner I chat to one of the teachers: Mrs Potts. She's very nice, with long, flame hair and a soft, catlike smile, she's my favourite teacher. I talk to her about what I want to be when I grow up: a doctor, and ask her how difficult it is to become a doctor. I even show off the fact that I know Einstein's formula for relativity: $E = mc^2$, although I get caught out when she asks me to explain it.

It's twilight now and I go back to the hut. I hate the dusk, it always makes me feel depressed. When I enter the dormitory some of Jan's gang are lounging around their beds, they look at me as I enter and they snigger. I look at my suitcase – it's been broken open. I open the lid and find the cha sui pork and roast duck spread all over my clothes and comics. One of the boys can't suppress his laughter anymore and bursts into a hysterical cackle. I march up to him and ask who did it. He tells me it was Jan and points to the next bunk where Jan's jacket is lying on the rough blanket covering the upper bed. Before I know it I've grabbed the mattress and pulled it to the floor. I stamp on the white sheets with my dirty shoes, leaving brown marks and bits of grit all over the starched, bleached cotton. There's a shocked silence from the rest of the boys then the boy who was laughing begins to taunt me: 'You're going to get it – Jan's going to beat the shit out of you now, he's going to f***ing kill you.'

I'm holding back the tears and yell 'I don't care', as I leave the dormitory. Jan walks in just as I'm about to leave. I turn and watch him as he walks to his bunk and then sees his overturned mattress. He runs over to me swearing, pointing his fingers at me, his face snarling. His finger jabs me in my chest as he asks my why I did what I did to his bed and I begin to retreat further outside the dormitory, stuttering and stammering that he had started it by breaking into my suitcase. The rest of the boys are following us as we move outside onto the entrance to the hut where the electric light blinks on as the light continues to fade from the day. A crowd gathers around us as I'm backed against the railing, Jan's finger still prodding at me, the tears building up behind my eyes which feel like they're ready to burst.

Some of Jan's mates are egging him on, telling him to hit me, to finish me off. Daniel tells Jan to leave me alone, but Jan turns aggressively and warns Daniel to mind his own business, calling him Jewboy again. Daniel shrinks into the crowd and now I've got Jan's full attention again. He starts to slap me across the face, I catch his hand, it's hard and muscular. He pulls it free and tries to slap me with the other hand. I catch his wrist and stop him again. He's shorter than me, he looks like a ferret or a stoat. I can see hate in his eyes as he frees his wrist and there are some boys telling me to hit back, to defend myself. I see Paul looking at me, mouthing the words 'Hit him!', making a fist and swiping the air in front of him. I look at Jan, he throws a punch and once again I intercept it – I catch his fist. Jan yells at me: 'Trying some of that kung fu shit? Can you do karate then?' I feel a tear begin to burst through and then Jan punches me in the mouth. His fist feels numb and cold and as I blink in shock my lips and teeth ache. The next thing I see is Jan's mouth sucking and moving like he was chewing cud. He spits and the saliva hits my face with more force than the punch. My tear ducts explode and I run off, through the crowd, Jan's last words ringing in my ears: 'So much for your Hong Kong phooey karate, you f***ing chink.'

A couple of hours had passed since I'd run out of the camp. I'd seen a few teachers and boys come looking for me with their torchlights and umbrellas. I was moving around from one bus shelter to another, trying to keep out of the rain, trying to stop crying. Eventually, the rain stopped. I was under a tree by the side of the road. I looked up at the dashes of drizzle highlighted under the yellow haze of a nearby streetlight. The tears were coming. My mouth swelled and blubbered uncontrollably. I asked myself why I hadn't fought back, I felt ashamed of myself and told myself to run further, to never go back. How could I face anyone there again? I started to feel cold and thought of my family, of my parents and how they would worry if I disappeared. My courage and my anger melted away and I began to walk back to the camp.

ABOUT THE WEDDING FEAST

By Ama Ata Aidoo

Outcomes

Discussion of Issues

The generation gap
Weddings
Family relationships
Conflict and resolution

Literacy Work

Text level
Dramatic exploration of the narrator's viewpoint **TB 70** **TB 71**

Sentence Level
Capturing a character's 'voice'
First person narrative, reported speech and rhetorical
questions **TB 69**

Word level
Comparative imagery **TB 72**

Drama and Oral Activities

Use of 'thought tracking' convention to explore the
contrast between public speech and inner thought **TB 70** **TB 71**

Stimulus page

Weddings – many cultures have ceremonies to celebrate the union of two people. Use the resources available to you (library/resource centre, the Internet, your RE teacher, people in your class or local community) and find out as much as you can about weddings in different cultures. Present your findings to your class.

Weddings often involve guests indulging in a feast. Make a list of the different types of food which might be found in these different ceremonies.

How has the idea of 'marriage' changed over the years? Do some research by asking older members of your family or friends about marriage, and discuss your findings in your group.

Grandparents often say things like, 'It was better in my day because . . .' Work in groups of three or four and devise a short list of typical sayings by grandparents.

Sometimes at weddings, when people are tense or over-excited, conflict emerges. As a pair, try and think of any weddings (even TV soap weddings) when this has happened. Share your stories. Now read on . . .

ABOUT THE WEDDING FEAST

By Ama Ata Aido

(With a little warning for all those who may be allergic to the genre: that this is 'kitchen literature' with a vengeance – AAA)

It had began with the announcement itself. That those two were going to get married. My granddaughter just came in from her workplace one early evening and told us. No asking. It was all telling. That was when something hit me. Yes, from that early. That there was something not right already. In the old days, when things were done properly, a girl did not just announce that sort of thing in that sort of way. But later, when I pointed out to the child's mother, my daughter Mary, she said that things have changed.

. . . Hei, and how they have changed! . . . And of course, being my daughter Mary, hard as a palm kernel outside and coconut-soft inside, she later came and without apologising for speaking like that to me, asked me how the young lady should have informed us about what she and her young man intended . . .

And then there was the matter of the time. How can a serious discussion like marriage intentions start at the end of the day? In the old days, if a young woman wanted to bring up such a matter, she would begin by just hinting one of her mothers on her mother's side, who would hint her mother, who would then have hinted me her grandmother, and then I and her mother would have discreetly mentioned it to any other mothers and grandmothers whom we considered close enough to be brought into the discussions and the negotiations that would follow. Then, very early the next morning – at dawn really – we would have had a meeting, in my room certainly, sitting down properly, of course . . . But here I go again, forgetting that things have changed! In this case, the young lady came to just tell us. And that was how everything got handled. In the modern, educated way, and not at all properly.

Maybe, I should not have let myself grieve: since for a start, we were in a foreign land. The young man my granddaughter was going to marry is from one part of Africa that is quite far from our country. My daughter Mary had sent me a ticket to go and visit her and her husband and children. Indeed, let me tell the truth: when it comes to such gestures, Mary is good . . . so I had gone. As everybody knows, this was the second or third time. In fact, I was preparing to return home here when the announcement came from my grandchild. That was a blessing. Because, the way things have changed, I could sense that they were going to go ahead and finalise everything, when no one at home had the slightest knowledge about the proposed marriage. And then, what was I going to tell everybody when I came back? You would all have laughed at me, no? That I too had gone and lost my head abroad: the way all these educated people seem to do when they travel overseas.

So I said to Mary my daughter: 'Mary, it is true that things have changed, but have they really changed that much?'

'Maybe not, Mother . . . you only worry too much,' was what she said. Now tell me, what kind of a response was that?

Anyway, that was when I came back here and informed you all about it. I had been quite surprised and very relieved that you had all been so understanding. Was it you or Abanowa who had suggested that since the child was in a foreign land anyway, and the young man she was marrying does not come from anywhere around here, everybody should accept that there was no question of anybody getting the chance to go and check his background to make sure everything about him and his family was satisfactory, and so if I found him acceptable, that should be fine with you all? At the time, I had not commented on it, but oh, I was so grateful for that.

As I had informed you all at the family meeting, I knew Mary was going to be sending me a ticket to go back there for the wedding. But she had sent it much earlier . . . Mary doesn't know how to do a lot of things. In that she is not alone. It's the education. It takes away some very important part of understanding from them . . . But then, I must also say for Mary that those things she knows how to do, she does them very well.

So, that was how I came to be present at the big meeting between Mary and the boy's mother about what should be prepared for the wedding feast . . . To tell the truth, I had not really felt too happy at the idea of a joint discussion. It was not right. What self-respecting family in the old days would ask for help from their prospective in-laws? Whether it was in the way of just ideas or for something more substantial like the actual preparation of the food for the wedding feast? But when I so much as opened my mouth, Mary said that these days, that is not only all right, but even expected. She added that in fact, she might hurt feelings if she didn't ask for the help. Mmm, things have really changed, haven't they?

Since there was not going to be any grandmother from the boy's side at the meeting, Mary and I agreed that I would sit in on the discussions, but would keep a respectable silence. Which is what I did. However, every now and then, my daughter whispered questions to me to which I gave discreet answers.

It had not seemed as if there was much disagreement about anything. They had discussed everything in a friendly way: the wedding cake itself; other cakes; biscuits and buns; how to do the peanuts and the other things for the guests to munch and crunch . . .

Peanuts? O yes, they are everywhere! . . .

They had sat and talked for a long time, may be for as much as half the day, when they came to the foods that called for real cooking. That was when things began to take time to decide. I had been thinking, and even told them, that if they did not stop for a little rest and get something to eat, something nasty was going to happen. But Mary said, and it was plain the boy's mother agreed with her, that it was better to finish everything at a sitting. I was going to open my mouth and tell them that since the beginning of creation, no family had finished planning what should go into a wedding feast at one sitting. But then I remembered that things had changed, and warned my lips.

Then it happened and I was not at all surprised. I had heard Mary mention jolof and other dishes from our country. Then maybe, for just the shortest bit of time, I had got lost in my own thoughts and had not paid attention to the discussions. Because I had not noticed that something had come up which was really cutting their tempers short. All I saw was suddenly, Mary and the boy's mother standing up at the same time and each of them shouting:

'That's no food and you are not serving it at my daughter's wedding.'

'That's no food and you are not serving it at my son's wedding.'

'Spinach stewed with a mixture of meat and fish?' shouted one with a sneer that was big enough to wither a virgin forest.

'Spinach stewed with only onions and without meat or fish?' shouted the other, the contempt in her voice heavy enough to crush a giant.

'What do you mean?' shouted one.

'What do you mean?' countered the other.

'I said that's no food, and you are not going to serve it at my child's wedding!' they both screamed at the same time.

'You cannot tell me that,' one wailed.

'You cannot tell me that,' the other whined after her.

'Our guests will not eat that,' one spat out.

'Our guests will laugh at us if you serve that,' said the other.

'They will tell everyone in our community.'

'They will write home to everyone in our country about it.'

'It is awful, a mess.'

'Yours is unclean.'

'Yours is completely tasteless.'

'But you ate it when you came to our house!' said one, perplexed.

'But you ate it when you came to our house!' said the other, equally perplexed.

'No, I didn't. I didn't touch it,' they both confessed.

'Eh?!'

'I went and threw it into the rubbish bin in the kitchen.'

'W-h-a-t?'

They made as if they were going to clutch at each other's throats.

'Mother, Mother, what is this?'

None of us who were already in the room had seen or felt my granddaughter and the young man come in. But they had.

'What is this?' they repeated. The mothers stopped dead. Shame on their faces, each stared at the girl and the boy in the hallway. For what seemed to be a very long time, there was complete silence. Then the boy and the girl looked at one another, burst out laughing, didn't stay to say anything else to anybody and then went out of the room, still laughing.

What did the mothers do? What could they do? Each of them just sat down and stayed sat. And quiet. After some time, I called my daughter Mary's name.

'What is it?' she asked, glaring at me.

'Listen,' I said, my voice low. 'I think you people had better stop now and continue with the planning of the feast tomorrow.'

'What is there to plan? . . . Anyway, I am finished with all that,' Mary said. And with that she went out of the room.

And that's how everything ended with the food affair. O yes, there was a wedding. And it was not only the ceremony itself that went well. Everything else was wonderful. We cooked our palaver sauce of spinach with egusi, meat and fish. The boy's people cooked their very plain spinach, without meat or fish . . . And did the guests eat? Don't even ask. They ate and ate and ate and ate. Since then, I have not heard that anyone from the boy's side complained about the food we cooked. And I am not hearing anyone from our side complain about the food our in-laws cooked . . .

You see o . . . what still puzzles me is how people can tell others how much things have changed, when they do not prepare their own minds to handle such changes, eh?! . . . And as my mother used to say: 'What is food anyway? Once it goes down the throat . . .'